INDIA'S TECHADE

INDIA'S TECHADE

DIGITAL REVOLUTION AND CHANGE IN
THE WORLD'S LARGEST DEMOCRACY

NALIN
MEHTA

WESTLAND
NON-FICTION

WESTLAND
NON-FICTION

First published by Westland Non-Fiction, an imprint of Westland Books, a division of Nasadiya Technologies Private Limited, in 2023

No. 269/2B, First Floor, 'Irai Arul', Vimalraj Street, Nethaji Nagar, Alapakkam Main Road, Maduravoyal, Chennai 600095

Westland, the Westland logo, Westland Non-Fiction and the Westland Non-Fiction logo are the trademarks of Nasadiya Technologies Private Limited, or its affiliates.

Copyright © Nalin Mehta, 2023

Nalin Mehta asserts the moral right to be identified as the author of this work.

ISBN: 9789357767972

10 9 8 7 6 5 4 3 2 1

CONTENTS

CONTENTS

INDIA'S DIGITAL TECHADE
AN INTRODUCTION

This is a small book about big disruptions. In the age of ChatGPT and AI, digital disruptions are often seen as synonymous with the American Silicon Valley or, more broadly, with the West. Even more so, with private companies like, say, Google or Meta. Yet, India's digital revolution is unlike any that came before. It was largely created through the actions of the State and public institutions. In a country of over a billion, it went viral on a scale that is unprecedented. It deeply disrupted the way Indians deal with money, with each other and with the government.

Over two decades, and across two different political regimes, the world's largest democracy combined the rise of cheap mobile phones, cheap data and a unique digital ID system to create an unprecedented revolution in digital public goods. This included the rise of path-breaking fintech systems like Unified Payments Interface (UPI), the creation of a new kind of welfare state based on digital direct benefit transfers and inter-linked e-governance systems that brought in almost half a billion people who never had bank accounts into the financial system.

Digital India changed the basic plumbing that underlies Indian society, transforming politics, the government's relationship with every Indian and the nature of the State itself.

This book pieces together how India created the digital revolution using the software infrastructure loosely called 'India Stack', leading to what Prime Minister Narendra Modi has called 'India's Techade'.[1]

It is a revolution that has profound implications for the rest of the world and for the future of Global Tech itself.

In a little over a decade, India built a melange of public digital platforms that have transformed lives. This India Stack, or Digital Public Infrastructure (DPI), is held up by three pillars: identity, payments and data management. Its base was laid with the Aadhaar biometric identity system created under the Manmohan Singh-led Congress government in 2009. By December 2022, India had 1.35 billion Aadhaar enrolments.2

This was followed by the building of systems like UPI, which made digital payments as easy as sending an SMS on your mobile phone or scanning a QR code. In May 2023, India recorded 9.4 billion UPI transactions worth Rs 14,89,145 crore. UPI accounted for as much as 73 per cent of all non-cash retail transactions.[3] To put this in perspective in global terms, this meant that India was now home to 46 per cent of the world's real-time digital payment transactions.[4]

The third pillar is focused on data services like DigiLocker, through which people can access authenticated government-verified documents like their driving licence, education records, tax records and so on. By December 2023, India had more than 137 million users of DigiLocker and over 5.62 billion documents had been made available through this platform from 2,311 issuer organisations.[5]

Such digital public platforms are game-changing not only for India. Their success has meant that many other countries have shown interest in using them. At last count, as many as forty-three countries had expressed an interest in using some aspects of this new Indian DPI, as a senior Indian cabinet minister told me in early 2023.

Such is the interest in this new Indian export that it has also become an important marker of the country's soft power. In a year in which India is hosting the G20, *The Economist*, for example, goes so far as to call India's punt on DPI its 'low-cost, software-based version of China's infrastructure-led Belt and Road Initiative'.[6]

Google's CEO Sundar Pichai says that Prime Minister Modi's 'vision for Digital India was ahead of its time. I now see it as a blueprint other countries are looking to do. And the follow-through on the scaling up of India's digital stack is a model that other countries are thinking about. It is something that will be very important in the G20 as well that is happening in India'.[7] And it's not just Pichai. Digital India has become a global talking point, having caught the attention of the world's tech and policy leaders, from Bill Gates and Microsoft's Satya Nadella to the World Bank and the International Monetary Fund (IMF).

This is why India has also made its focus on DPI a crucial priority for its presidency of the G20.[8] As Modi told G20 leaders in Bali in November 2022:

Digital transformation is the most remarkable change of our era ... Unfortunately, till now we have seen this powerful tool only from the criteria of simple business, keeping this power tied in the ledgers of profit and loss. It is the responsibility of us G-20 leaders that the benefits of digital transformation should not be confined to a small part of the human race ...

India has developed digital public goods whose basic architecture has in-built democratic principles. These solutions are based on open source, open APIs, open standards, which are interoperable and public. This is our approach based on the digital revolution that is going on in India today.[9]

India's digital public infrastructure model is different from the Big Tech model of the US, or the General Data Protection Regulation (GDPR) model of Europe, India's G20 sherpa Amitabh Kant has argued.[10] Globally, he pointed out, 133 countries do not have a digital fast payments system, 4 billion people do not have a digital identity and two-and-a-half billion people do not have a bank account. 'How do we take this model of India to the world is the challenge and we will use the G-20 narrative to push this digital transformation story of India to the rest of the world and how we can transform the lives of citizens in the Global South.'[11]

A phalanx of Indian non-profit or public organisations had begun exporting these services by 2023. The National Payments Corporation (NPCI), a public–private partnership helmed by the Reserve Bank of India, which runs UPI, set up NPCI International Payments Limited (NIPL) in 2020 to roll out India's domestic card scheme (RuPay) within the country and UPI (mobile payments) in global markets.[12]

By early 2023, for example, UPI was connected with Singapore's PayNow system. Also with the United Arab Emirates, through Mashreq Bank's NEOPAY system. Nepal and Bhutan have been using UPI since 2022. Agreements have been signed for deploying UPI in France and several other European countries as well.[13]

Similarly, several countries like the Philippines, Morocco, Burkina Faso, Ethiopia, Togo, Ethiopia and Sri Lanka had begun using or signed agreements for creating an Aadhaar-like unique digital identity system, using the Modular Open Source Identity Platform (MOSIP) developed by Bangalore's International Institute of Information Technology as a global public good.[14]

Domestically, the rise of digital public infrastructure meant that India significantly expanded the scale and scope of its welfare state between 2013 and 2023 through direct benefit transfers. Government data shows that the initial 10.8 crore beneficiaries of Direct Benefit Transfer (DBT) reported in 2013–14 (many of whom were added under UPA) went up by over eight times to 92.3 crore beneficiaries by 2022–23. Actual direct cash payments into people's bank accounts went up by over thirty-four times from Rs 7,367 crore in 2013–14 to Rs 2.55 lakh crore in 2022–23. If you add transfers in kind (such as food grains under the public distribution system), then total transfers went up by more than a whopping 110 times in the same period. This seismic shift was possible because India used Aadhaar to open over 462 million new bank accounts for the poor in eight years.[15] In other words, this digital transformation also changed the nature of the relationship between the State and the poor.

How did these shifts occur in the world's most populous country? What did India do? What do these changes mean? What do they portend for the future? These are the questions these pages seek to answer.

Digital India may be a buzzword, but the word 'digital' is an amorphous one. It means different things to different people. This is also true for 'Digital India', the flagship government scheme launched by Narendra Modi's government on 1 July 2015, after he first articulated the vision for it in his inaugural Independence Day speech as prime minister from the ramparts of the Red Fort in 2014.

This book is not a story of individual government schemes. Instead, it focuses on the bigger story of India's digital transformation. Part 1 focuses on the 'The Build'—how India built the superstructure on which its digital public infrastructure was then created. Part 2 focuses on 'The Play'—how this played out for India's poor and created a new kind of welfare state. Part 3 is about UPI—how it transformed the economy and its 'Hinges'. Part 4 looks at the hardware and the nuts and bolts of India's digital transformation.

Based on on- and off-the-record conversations with key players, including politicians, technocrats, policymakers, bureaucrats, business tycoons, public and private agencies and scores of foot soldiers who contributed to the making of this Indian techade, the book seeks to do a status check. To pull together the story so far of the momentous and far-reaching nature of the fascinating digital shift we are currently seeing unfolding in India.

1

THE BUILD

THE INSIDE STORY OF AADHAAR AND INDIA'S DIGITAL SCAFFOLDING

Soothing santoor music played in the background. Two sitars—one big, the other one small—were placed tastefully. On the walls was a colourful painting, an allegory for the freedom struggle. It depicted a bull being pulled by two men.

I was waiting for my appointment with Prime Minister Narendra Modi in the anteroom at his official residence on 7 Lok Kalyan Marg in Delhi. The room was in a corner of his sanctum, past a pillared grand portico adorned with two imposing rows of the Indian tricolour, three flags in each row. In the corridor outside, a grand bronze statue of a dancing Nataraj, a depiction of Shiva as the divine cosmic dancer doing the tandava, completed the cultural framing of the PM's residence.

I had just started sipping my green tea, delivered by a white-gloved attendant, when the PM's Officer on Special Duty (OSD) hurriedly rushed in to say it was time.

When we walked in, the prime minister was sitting flanked by two stunning eighteenth-century paintings. One of the watercolours depicted the lower temple of Tritchengur. The other was of Gincee, Madras. Both paintings, with their place-name legends in the quaint style of the East India Company period, were by Thomas Danielle, a British painter who spent seven years in India, painting a six-volume series of paintings called 'Oriental Scenery'. Modi's chair was decorated with the Ashokan lions, the symbol of Indian sovereignty. Painted across the entire ceiling was a brilliantly vivid map of the world.

To my first query on his perspective on India's digital payments revolution, Modi answered with a reference to his pet project of the Gujarat International Finance Tec-City (GIFT City) by the banks of the Sabarmati river in his home state.

Inaugurated on 29 July 2022, and home to the first India International Bullion Stock Exchange (IIBX) as well as its first International Financial Services Authority, the Tec-City had been created with the explicit aim of rivalling financial hubs in the UAE, Singapore and Hong Kong. 'When I imagined the GIFT City in 2007, nobody had even imagined then,' said Modi. A fintech world needed a fintech city.[1]

As he would later say publicly, in his speech at the inauguration ceremony near Gandhinagar:

> Indians have a long tradition in mathematics. India invented the concept of 'zero' and the 'decimal system' more than two thousand years ago. It is no accident that Indians are now at the forefront of Information Technology and Finance, both areas of knowledge where zero plays a crucial role! When the Gift city was conceptualised, I was chief minister of Gujarat ... We had world class talent of Indian origin working in India and abroad. India had a leadership position in Information Technology. Finance was being increasingly married to technology. It was becoming very clear to us that finance combined with technology, or 'fintech' as it is sometimes called, would be an important part of India's future development ...
>
> India is in an excellent time zone between the West and the East. It can provide financial services through the day and night to the entire world. The exchange, I am told, will work twenty-

two hours a day, starting when the Japanese markets start, and closing when US markets close.[2]

As he warmed up to the theme, I asked him about Aadhaar, India's unique ID system, the largest in the world. 'Ask Nandan Nilekani,' he said. And then, he added with a twinkle in his eye, 'I opposed Aadhaar when I was chief minister of Gujarat.'

The prime minister, by this time, in April 2022, had spent eight years in office putting his full political weight behind Aadhaar. It was the fulcrum of his work on retooling the Indian welfare state, creating the digital payments network, UPI, and also of much of his government's focus on digitisation. Yet, he was prepared to go back to the beginnings and talk about his early misgivings before he won office in Delhi.

Nilekani, the Bengaluru billionaire and co-founder as well as chairman of Infosys, the IT multinational with a US$100-billion capitalisation, had built Aadhaar in his role as the founding chairman of the Unique Identification Authority of India (UIDAI). It was created in 2009 by the previous Congress government of Manmohan Singh and Nilekani famously left Infosys for public service, after initially being offered the role of human resources minister in the United Progressive Alliance (UPA) government.

Aadhaar, meaning 'foundation' or 'base' in Hindi, was conceived simply as a twelve-digit identification system with the narrow purpose of easing welfare payments. Under Modi, it expanded in quantum terms. It became the bedrock for enabling a whole host of services, including the game-changing UPI, which turned India into the world's largest hub for digital payments.

How Modi came to put so much behind Aadhaar, against the previously stated position of his own party until 2014, and then doubled down on it, is a unique story of policymaking. How two different regimes, bitterly opposed to each other ideologically, backed the unique ID project because they saw its benefits—even if they implemented it very differently—is a tale that must enthuse every democrat and every Indian.

Modi was telling me the backstory of this fascinating tale and his thinking on Aadhaar. 'I didn't oppose the idea of Aadhaar,' he said. 'I opposed the product and the way they said it will work. I said you will face these problems on the ground. We had many meetings, Nandan and I, in Gujarat. I had ground experience and could tell him where it wouldn't work. I am not a technical person, but because of my experience I could see where they would run into problems on the ground. In the end, they found 100 per cent solutions to the issues I had raised and he accepted it.'

As the PM put it, 'I don't have a tech solution. I am not an expert. I told him only where Aadhaar would fail, based on my ground experience. After the first meeting, he returned. I wasn't opposing it. He wanted sudhaar [improvement] for Aadhaar, a solution that worked. It came up in our discussion and he agreed. He and his team found the solutions to the issues I had raised.'

You ask Nandan, he emphasised, telling me not to take what he said at face value.

As it happened, I had indeed asked Nandan the same question six years earlier. We were speaking at the Times Lit Fest 2016, which I had co-curated. The Infosys czar delivered the keynote address on 'India@70: Rebooting the Republic'.

As one of the few self-made titans of corporate India, Nilekani was a rockstar who always got a full house. The auditorium at Delhi's India Habitat Centre was packed to capacity. It was just two weeks after the Modi government's decision to demonetise Rs 500 and Rs 1,000 notes, taking over 80 per cent of Indian money out of circulation. Nilekani was one of India's greatest evangelists for a digital economy. UPI was still a flashy techie acronym that few had heard of. India Stack was only a buzzword that most people in the audience had never heard of. And the DBT revolution was just about taking off. All of this was based on Aadhaar.

On stage, before a packed Delhi audience, Nilekani described the moment when it all changed for Aadhaar.

But first, the context. In 2014, Nilekani, who had enjoyed cabinet rank in Manmohan Singh's government, stood as a Congress candidate from Bangalore South against the BJP's stalwart, the late Ananth Kumar. The richest candidate in all of India,[3] the self-made technocrat billionaire from IIT Bombay and darling of corporate India, was directly opposed by the BJP's PM face. Narendra Modi himself campaigned against him in Bengaluru.[4] Nilekani went under in the Modi wave that changed Indian politics forever.

The Congress defeat put a huge question mark over the future of Aadhaar. Shortly after the BJP's victory, a party spokesperson publicly said, 'Our concerns are two-fold: the lack of a legal backing and security concerns.' There was a great deal of speculation about what would happen to the unique ID project.

Amid the jostling, Nilekani, who was in Delhi to hand over his government-allotted house, sought an appointment with the prime minister. To his great surprise, he was given time within twenty-four hours.[5]

As one former official with knowledge of the matter told me, the backstory was that Aadhaar, launched by the UPA government, was then in limbo. The BJP had opposed it during its election campaign. When Modi got elected as prime minister on 16 May in a landslide victory, he inherited a dispute between different ministries.

The National Democratic Alliance (NDA) government resolved it and took a call on the future of Aadhaar itself. As the official explained, 'One of the reasons why it was struck in the previous government was because the then Planning Commission (later Niti Aayog) [through the Unique Identification Authority of India, created as its attached office] and the Home Ministry were doing two parallel projects. Both required an identity system. Both required verification. The Finance Ministry was backing Aadhaar. The Home Ministry had its own citizen ID project for the National Population Register. These two parallel programmes were going on. And nobody was able to resolve it fully. That Aadhaar will become the final enabling identification, this the other ministry was not willing to accept. And parallel work was going on. When this government came to power, these issues came to a head and concerned stakeholders made presentations to put forward their point of view.'[6]

Before Nilekani's meeting with the PM, 'everybody else' had met the PM. 'There were a whole lot of meetings on this. A lot of presentations,' said the official.[7]

It was at this point that Nilekani was asked by the UIDAI chairman to meet the prime minister and make the case for it.[8]

'Nandan was initially reluctant,' said the official. 'He had contested in the elections. He had worn the Congress topi-vopi and campaigned against BJP in elections. Anyhow, when the BJP government came, Ravishankar-ji [Prasad, the then telecom and IT minister] would have briefed PM, the secretary would have briefed him. Others would have too. In that, a suggestion came. Nandan was asked to go and meet the PM. He was initially very reluctant. He asked, should he meet? The election had just finished and he had contested against BJP. Anyhow he went ... he went and met the PM and he realised the PM is different. He is looking at the product, he is not looking at it politically.'[9]

Nilekani himself recounted his memory of that fateful meeting. As he was to write six years later:

> I was passionate about the value of Aadhaar to India, and after encouragement from my wife and some friends, I decided to meet Prime Minister Modi and discuss the matter.
>
> Towards the end of June 2014, I was in New Delhi, wrapping up my home to return permanently to Bengaluru. I sought a

meeting with the new Prime Minister. To my utter astonishment I got an appointment within twenty-four hours at a time convenient to me. I went with some trepidation, as I had just stood for the election on a rival party's ticket. Modi was gracious and listened to me intently. This time his questions were about issuing the card to residents and not citizens, and how India's fiscal situation could benefit from direct benefit transfers (DBTs) and its role in reducing corruption. He was well informed on all issues, including the privacy case in the Supreme Court. What struck me was his openness to listen and to do what was right for the country.[10]

Recalling further details of the discussion, he says, 'It was evident to him [Modi] that linking an individual's mobile phone number, bank account and Aadhaar card could yield several advantages to beneficiaries and to the several arms of government at the Union and state levels that were vested in delivering benefits to citizens.'[11] Nilekani also argued that not only would the system benefit DBT but it could also save the exchequer Rs 50,000 crore by removing duplicates.[12]

Modi and Nilekani met on 1 July 2014. There is enough evidence to show that this meeting changed the fate of Aadhaar. Also at the meeting was the then finance minister, the late Arun Jaitley.

Why did Modi meet Nilekani? And did he take credit for adopting something that the previous regime had built? This was the first question to the IT tycoon from the jam-packed Delhi audience that day. The question came from a prominent English TV journalist and anchor who stood up and asked why Nilekani had met a political leader who had campaigned against him and critiqued the Aadhaar programme earlier.

Nilekani's first response was to smile. He joked laconically that he was 'not sitting in your television studio'. Then, his expression became dead serious. 'I think I am happy that Aadhaar has not only been adopted, it has been accelerated by the Modi government,' he said slowly and with precision. After a short pause, he added, 'I am happy because my first loyalty is to Aadhaar.' That line brought the house down.

'The fact that it has revived and thrived even in a major political transition is good news for me,' he continued. 'For me, the success of the project was paramount, because it is something that I had invested five years of my life in and I wanted it to succeed. So, I am happy at that. And yes, if we are able to achieve the vision we have laid out, we will absolutely answer your queries and be able to take the bureaucracy out of the lives of farmers in the villages.'[13]

The meeting in Delhi was not, as we know, the first occasion when the technocrat and the politician had met. When Nilekani was canvassing support with state governments for Aadhaar as the chairman of UIDAI, he had first met Modi, then Gujarat chief minister, in July 2011.

He later substantiated the point Modi made to me on his discussions with the IT tycoon on the improvements needed in the ID system and the debate they had at the time. Recalling that first meeting, Nilekani wrote, 'I noticed how spick and span his office was. A thirty-minute meeting went on for ninety minutes on how he had done development innovations in Gujarat and the many ways he was using technology. I did not have to explain much about Aadhaar. Of all my visits to various states and meetings with several chief ministers, he was the only one who had understood that the Aadhaar document would reach 1.3 billion Indian residents, and, therefore, what was printed on the card was of strategic importance.'[14]

The scheme's slogan then, 'Aam Aadmi ka Adhikaar' (the Right of the Ordinary Citizen), was often used as a Congress party slogan at the time. Nilekani emphasised that only two people had noticed this: Narendra Modi and Sonia Gandhi.

As he told the journalist Sonia Singh, 'When I met Mr Modi, he said, "Aapne Congress ka slogan kyon use kiya? [Why have you used a Congress slogan?].'" He went on to say, 'One day, Mrs Gandhi told me she was concerned I was using BJP colours on the Aadhaar letter which was being sent to people, to which I said it was using the national flag colours. I had to get samples to show her that they were indeed the national flag colours. Here was a card going to a billion people so obviously one would be concerned about the text, symbols and colours on it. Yet, to my astonishment, only Mrs Sonia Gandhi and Mr Modi in the entire system asked me about it!'[15]

Things moved quickly after the Modi–Nilekani meeting on 1 July 2014.

Two days later, on 3 July, the prime minister met Home Minister Rajnath Singh, Telecom and IT Minister Ravi Shankar Prasad, the UIDAI chairman, the registrar general of India, the home secretary, the planning commission secretary, Planning Minister Rao Inderjeet Singh and the principal secretary to the prime minister. As an official privy to the meeting told me:

> Ultimately, he asked the citizen waalas who were from the home ministry, do you want identity? They said yes, we want it. He said how you will identify identity, that it is correct or wrong. They said with biometric means. So, he asked, how will you collect biometrics? What they said, Aadhaar was already doing. So, the PM said, then why are you doing it separately? They didn't have any answer.
>
> Then he asked the biometric people, the Aadhaar team. Can your database be used for this without biometrics being leaked to identify people if we want benefits? They said, yes, it can be done.
>
> Ultimately, he said, both of you go and discuss. Come back in one week. Only one system of the two will remain. Which one will remain, you decide and come back to me. They both went back. After one week, both agreed that Aadhaar is the system that will remain.[16]

Four days later, on 5 July 2014, Modi sought a Rs 100-crore enrolment target under Aadhaar at the 'earliest', 'casting aside earlier notions that the new government will go slow on the UIDAI project'. Nine days after the Modi–Nilekani meeting, Finance Minister Arun Jaitley increased the allocation for Aadhaar from Rs 1,550 crore to Rs 2,039 crore.[17]

Jaitley was asked to create legislative backing for Aadhaar and to begin work on a new bill.[18] This was eventually passed in 2016 as a money bill.[19] Crucially, the ambit of Aadhaar expanded significantly from what it was under the UPA. By October 2014, for instance, it included seven major new schemes:

- Mandatory biometric attendance at work for government officials.
- Linking to passports, mobile SIM cards and provident fund accounts.
- Prisoner identification.
- Digital India project to serve as a cradle-to-grave digital identity.
- Cash transfers for cooking gas to be restarted in fifty-four districts to begin with, then to the rest of the country. These had initially been stopped due to an earlier Supreme Court ruling which said Aadhaar could not be mandatory.[20]

Interestingly, Aadhaar's biggest endorsement came from the Home Ministry, which had been its aggressive opponent even under Rajnath Singh. In a letter to all state governments, the ministry said an Aadhaar number would facilitate 'anytime, anywhere, anyhow authentication to beneficiaries'. 'As more and more government services are going to be linked to Aadhaar, it will be of utility to have an Aadhaar card. Aadhaar will, hence, help the poor to take the benefits or the facilities provided to them by the government that could not be accessed [by them] earlier. Aadhaar will become the simplest way of proving one's identity,' the letter said.[21]

Aadhaar's expansion also led to a passionate and bitter public debate between those who supported the unique digital ID system as a tool for social welfare and as a symbol of the digital economy versus those who saw it as an invasion of their right to privacy and apprehended the creation of a 'totalitarian state' based on a 'surveillance society'.

This visceral argument was finally settled by the Supreme Court of India in 2018.

Noting that Aadhaar had spread like 'wildfire' and virtually become a 'household symbol', a five-member constitution bench of the apex court ruled by a 4:1 majority that the legislation that enabled the unique ID system—the Aadhaar (Targeted Delivery of Financial and Other Subsidies, Benefits and Services) Act, 2016— was constitutionally valid. The court declared that, on balance, the Aadhaar programme served 'the larger public interest', but struck down some of its provisions.[22]

Looking back, as Nilekani later concluded, Modi's pivotal decision to put his entire political weight behind Aadhaar and to scale it up changed everything.

'He (Modi) was one of the persons who really made it happen. He was the biggest sponsor of Aadhaar and today it has reached every nook and corner of India, has become a part of the JAM [Jan Dhan-Aadhaar-mobile] trinity and has become completely important in everybody's life. We have seen it even more during the pandemic when millions availed the benefits during the Aadhaar-based Direct Benefit Transfer (DBT).'[23]

This was how the battle for Aadhaar was won. National destinies are often based on personalities. This sequence of events shows exactly how.

2

THE BUILD, PART 2
CREATING A NEW DIGITAL 'RAILWAY' FOR INDIA

Malati Singh remembers being befuddled when she got the call. A family friend had approached her with a request sometime in 2012. An acquaintance had just been contracted as an enrolment agent by the recently created UIDAI to make Aadhaar cards. He was on the phone, asking if she would lend the premises of her family-run school in the industrial town of Kanpur to run an Aadhaar registration camp.

Singh wasn't sure what to expect. But the school was closing for summer vacations anyway. So she agreed to its classrooms being used for a one-month registration camp. 'I didn't expect the crowds,' she told me. 'I thought it would be very quiet, but the same excitement that people once used to have to get ration cards made, they seemed to have for Aadhaar. I was surprised to see long queues for hours in the school maidan daily.'

While the lines formed outside, the enrolment agents took up three classrooms inside. 'Sometimes there were fights also in the queue, if people were processed out of turn,' she said. 'Those who didn't have valid ID proof to register could do so by getting a signed written letter from the local parshad [municipal councillor] on his letterhead.'

Singh's institution, the Jag Narain Singh Memorial School, in Kanpur's Rawatpur suburb, at the periphery of the city limits, happened to be located at a strategic point where the city meets the rural hinterland. At least 15,000 people had signed up for Aadhaar cards at this school camp before the month was out, she recalls.

Enrolment drives like this one, run by hundreds of different kinds of authorised registrars—community service centres, private agents, banks, railways, state governments, public sector undertakings—eventually delivered India's great Aadhaar boom.[1] The authorised registrars, in turn, hired enrolment agencies. Like the one that contacted Malati Singh. Hired district by district, they did the work on the ground. Paid a nominal fee for every card that they registered, they had a business incentive to enrol as many people as they could. These were the foot soldiers who enabled the eventual spread of Digital India. By 2023, such methods had yielded 1.3 billion Aadhaar numbers.

By itself, Aadhaar may not have accounted for much. In a country with low connectivity, a unique ID system alone would have had very limited impact. Aadhaar retooled India because the political bet on the system and the pivotal decision to scale it up coincided with two other factors: India's mobile phone revolution which, in turn, led to a cheap data and internet revolution. The marriage of these two with a unique biometric ID system changed the basic plumbing that underlies Indian society, politics, the government's relationship with every Indian and the nature of the State itself.

By the 2019 elections, which marked Modi's second majority, India had the world's second-highest smartphone penetration[2] and the highest average data usage per smartphone, reaching 9.8 gigabytes (GB) per month.[3] By 2023, this had jumped, by one count, to 19.5 GB of data usage per Indian per month. For perspective, that is roughly the equivalent of downloading about 6,600 songs.[4]

So, first, India had a mobile phone revolution. This laid the basic foundation for everything. By 2017, almost every Indian had a mobile phone. My generation of Indians grew up in a country where landline phones were a luxury. Some of our most abiding memories were about getting phone messages from the one neighbour in the colony who was lucky enough to actually have a phone connection at their home. From the early 2000s onwards, India simply leapfrogged the landline stage.

The rise of the cheap mobile phone and the massive social transformation it engendered has been well documented by several scholars, most notably by Robin Jeffrey (National University of Singapore) and Assa Doron (Australian National University).[5] By 2022, India had 1.16 billion mobile connections and over 85 per cent phone penetration.[6] Landlines were just about 2 per cent of this. Today, to have a phone in India means to have a mobile.

Next came the cheap data and internet revolution.

From 2014 onwards, the year Modi came to power, data prices started to crash in India. This huge shift fuelled a massive jump in data consumption and internet access through cheap mobiles (see Figure 2.1). By 2022, India had the highest per capita data consumption in the world, more than Europe or North America.[7] Moreover, 1 GB of data now cost less than Rs 10. This was thirty times cheaper than what it cost in 2014, about Rs 300. In other words, the internet was now much more accessible for the poor.

By various estimates, an average Indian consumed between 14 and 19 GB of data a month in 2022. 'In 2014, the cost of this 14 GB data was around Rs 4,200 per month,' emphasised Modi at the India Mobile Congress. 'Today, the same amount of data is available for Rs 100 or Rs 150. That is, today about Rs 4,000 of the poor and the middle class is being saved every month on mobile data ... the cost of data in India remains very low. Saving 4,000 rupees every month is not a small thing.'[8]

Internet users in India increased eightfold through Modi's first term in office—from 65.3 million in May 2014 to nearly 600 million in May 2019. That number increased to over 800 million by 2022.[9] Even more significantly, Google reported that more than half of its searches were now coming from 'Bharat', or non-metro cities. This

Figure 2.1: India's Cheap Data Revolution through Mobiles

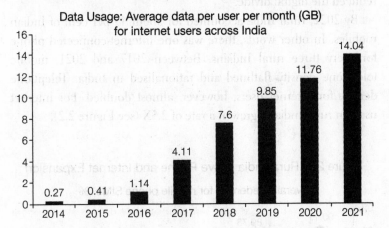

Data Price Crash: Effective cost per GB for internet users across India (Rs)

Data Usage: Average data per user per month (GB) for internet users across India

Source: Yearly data from Telecom Regulatory Authority of India, Government of India. Analysis by Rishabh Srivastava, DataNarratives, defog.ai.

was driven by the fact that India's average mobile data consumption per user was by then on par with developed markets.[10]

In just eight years, monthly data usage in the country increased by over seventy-five times, rising from 0.26 GB per person in 2014 to 19.5 GB per person in 2022.[11] This meant that roughly one in every three Indians was using apps or digital tools like Facebook (up from 9 per cent in 2014), WhatsApp or YouTube by the time of Modi's second national electoral triumph in 2019.[12]

This cheap data revolution, triggered by the launch of the Jio phone network in September 2016, also transformed Indian politics. Digital penetration figures show that widespread adoption of technology may have been the single biggest society-shifting event of the past decade, altering the neural structures of how society works.[13] From the Gutenberg press in medieval Europe, which powered the Reformation and the European Renaissance, to mobile phones, whenever a new mass technology has emerged, it has changed the nature of society and politics.[14] Moreover, rural India powered much of this growth of mobile internet connectivity. This significantly reduced the digital divide.

By 2022, rural India accounted for about 45 per cent of Indian mobiles. In other words, there was one internet-connected phone for every three rural Indians. Between 2017 and 2021, mobile telephone density flatlined and rationalised in India. Telephone density for internet users, however, almost doubled. For internet users in rural India, it grew at a rate of 2.5X (see Figure 2.2).

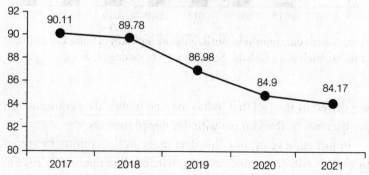

Figure 2.2: Rural India Drove Phone and Internet Expansion

Overall teledensity for mobile phone SIMs, %

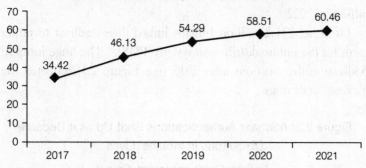

Overall teledensity for internet users, %

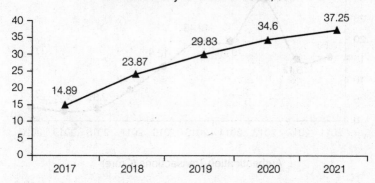

Rural teledensity for internet users, %

Source: Yearly data from Telecom Regulatory Authority of India, Government of India. Analysis by Rishabh Srivastava, DataNarratives, defog.ai.

Crucially, the Aadhaar revolution unfolded almost in tandem with these other three trends. Aadhaar, which acted as a bridge between online and offline activities, basically started as an identity document for all Indians. But after the digital revolution, it became the bedrock for a whole host of digital transactions.

During the Manmohan Singh government of 2009–14, generating more Aadhaar cards had become the government's main priority. By the time, Modi came to power in 2014, 700 million Aadhaar cards had been created.[15] His government's decision to double down on Aadhaar almost doubled that number to over 1.3 billion by 2022.

Of these, 731.2 million Indians linked their Aadhaar to ration cards for the public distribution system (PDS).[16] The huge jump in Aadhaar authentications after 2015 (see Figure 2.3) reflected the increase in its usage.

Figure 2.3: Aadhaar Authentications Shot Up as It Became Ubiquitous in Indians' Lives

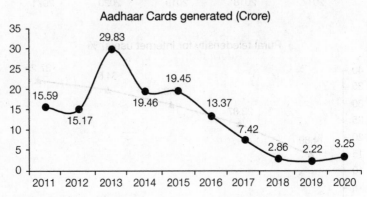

Aadhaar Cards generated (Crore)

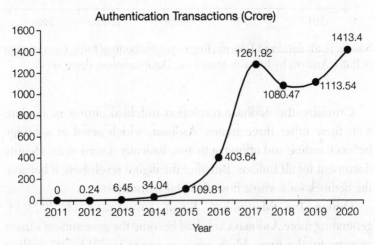

Authentication Transactions (Crore)

Source: Yearly data from Unique Identification Authority of India (UIDAI), Analysis by Rishabh Srivastava, DataNarratives, defog.ai.

Because of higher Aadhaar penetration, it was now used to make thousands of crores of authenticated transactions, including eKnow Your Customer (eKYC), UPI payments and more. For perspective on this, UIDAI reported a whopping 92.45 billion authentication transactions cumulatively by 2023.[17] About 40 per cent of these transactions came from the banking system for Aadhaar-enabled payment systems, 20 per cent from the PDS, about 6 per cent from telecom and 2 per cent from the Mahatma Gandhi National Rural Employment Guarantee Act (MGNREGA) scheme.[18]

A Bank Account for Every Indian: A Payments Revolution with JAM

Six weeks after that meeting between Modi and Nilekani in Delhi, the prime minister ascended the steps of the Red Fort in Delhi to deliver his maiden Independence Day speech on 15 August 2014. In this, his first public articulation of his governance vision since winning office, Modi broke convention by speaking extempore for sixty-five minutes, dispensing with the customary bulletproof screen and turning his speech into a soliloquy on his broader ideas on governance rather than a staid bureaucratic litany of governmental schemes.

Sporting a polka-dotted Gujarati red-and-green turban, Modi played the outsider card, explaining to a national audience how Delhi's elites looked upon him as an 'untouchable' and how he had found not one united government but many, with departments often fighting with each other rather than working as one.

All the usual touchpoints of the Modi model that were soon to become signature programmes of his government—Digital India, mobiles, Swachh Bharat and toilets—first featured in this inaugural Red Fort speech.

It was also the first time Modi spoke about the idea of the Pradhan Mantri Jan Dhan Yojana (Prime Minister's People Money Scheme). In a country where a majority of the citizens had never had a bank account, the scheme's ambition was sky high. It promised a zero-balance bank account, a debit card and an insurance safety net of Rs 100,000 to every poor Indian.[19]

With the Aadhaar pipeline in place, Modi now outlined the contours of the first grand expansion of social welfare and the financial inclusion that it was about to engender. Tellingly, he compared the mobile in the digital age to the railways in a previous era—a grand connector of the nation:

> Brothers and sisters, I have come here with a pledge to launch a scheme on this festival of Freedom. It will be called Pradhanmantri Jan Dhan Yojana. I wish to connect the poorest citizens of the country with the facility of bank accounts through this yojana. There are millions of families who have mobile phones but no bank accounts. We have to change this scenario. Economic resources of the country should be utilised for the well-being of the poor. The change will commence from this point. This yojana will open the window. Therefore, an account holder under 'Pradhanmantri Jan Dhan Yojana' will be given a debit card. An insurance of One Lakh Rupees will be guaranteed with that debit card for each poor family, so that such families are covered with the insurance of One Lakh Rupees in case of any crisis in their lives ...
>
> When I talk of 'Digital India', I don't speak of the elite, it is for the poor people ...
>
> The citizens of India have mobile phones in their hands, they have mobile connectivity, but can we walk in the direction of mobile governance? We have to move in a direction where every poor person is able to operate his bank account from his mobile, is able to demand various things from the government, can submit applications, can conduct all his business, while on the move, through mobile governance and if this has to be done, we have to move towards 'Digital India' and if we have to move towards 'Digital India' then we have a dream ...

There was a time when we used to say that the railways provided connectivity to the country. That was it. I say that today it is IT that has the potential to connect each and every citizen of the country and that is why we want to realise the mantra of unity with the help of 'Digital India'.[20]

The PM Jan Dhan Yojana scheme was formally launched two weeks later, on 28 August 2014. The results have been stunning.

Consider this. In eight years, India opened over 462 million new bank accounts for the poor. That's more than the entire population of the United States, France and UK put together (see charts in Figure 2.4). By any yardstick, this is an astonishing number for anyone interested in global financial inclusion. A Guinness world record started the Jan Dhan campaign — 18 million accounts in one week between 23 and 29 August 2014 — and it has grown consistently since. Crucially, over two-thirds of these accounts (308.9 million) are in rural and semi-urban areas. Over half (257.1 million) are in the names of women.[21]

Figure 2.4: Banking for the Poor: India's Financial Inclusion Revolution (2015–22)

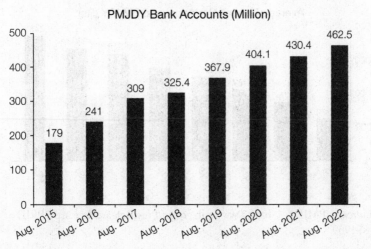

PMJDY Bank Accounts (Million)

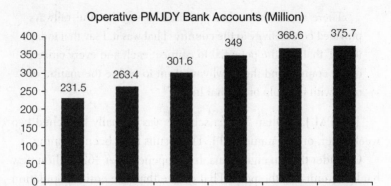

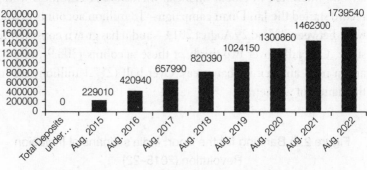

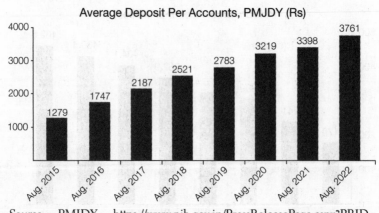

Source: PMJDY, https://www.pib.gov.in/PressReleasePage.aspx?PRID=1854909

These are mind-boggling numbers. How real are they? If you count operative accounts, that is, those that have had a transaction within the last two years, they amount to 375.5 million. Again, that is more than the population of the United States and Australia put together. Overall, between 2015 and 2022, account numbers increased three-fold, and the money in these increased by over seven times.

'The rest of the world could learn from developments over the past decade in Indian payments,' concluded *The Financial Times* in 2019.[22] Aadhaar 'sounds terrifyingly 1984 to us', the FT's International Economy News Editor Clair Jones noted. 'Leaving aside the very real ethical concerns and possibilities of data breaches, what we want to focus on here is that Aadhaar has provided a brilliant foundation for banking the unbanked. Which, without doubt, it has.'

Numbers like these explain why 'drum-beaters for financial inclusion have been excited about India', noted *The Economist* as well. The country had emerged as an 'important battleground for financial inclusion'.[23]

The excitement accrued from the fact that the introduction and expansion of the Jan Dhan Yojana 'coincided with a period of rapid increase in financial access, in which the percentage of [Indian] adults with a bank account increased from 35 per cent in 2011 to 80 per cent in 2017'.[24]

Research from the IMF emphasised that this was possible essentially because of 'the development of the digital infrastructure known as the "India Stack", including an interoperable payments system, a universal digital ID, and other features'.[25] 'India's journey in developing world-class DPI (digital public infrastructure)', an IMF working paper argued, 'highlights powerful lessons for other countries embarking on their own digital transformation'.[26]

The Bank of International Settlements (BIS) reached a similar conclusion. It noted in a detailed paper on the 'lessons from India' on the design for financial infrastructure that:

India offers an example of how various policy reforms related to digital finance—including transformation of the traditional banking system with the central bank playing a pivotal role—can solve many of the challenges of inclusive financial development that once seemed out of reach. It also offers insights into how the regulator (e.g. the central bank) and the regulated (e.g. commercial banks) can together run a payment system that operates around the clock, throughout the year, is open to participation of firms ranging from boutique fintechs to big techs and provides all the network benefits that big tech systems usually provide, but settles instantly in fiat money inside the central bank.

India's approach is built upon four pillars: (i) providing digital financial infrastructure as a public good; (ii) encouraging private innovation by providing open access to this infrastructure; (iii) creating a level playing field through the regulatory framework; and (iv) empowering individuals through a data-sharing framework that requires their consent. India offers important lessons that are equally relevant for advanced economies and emerging market and developing economies. [27]

Table 2.1: How India Bridged the Gap on Financial Inclusion with Aadhaar and UPI

	2011, India	2014, India	2017, India	2017, World
Percent with bank account	35%	53%	80%	67%
Gender gap	17%	20%	6%	7%
Men	44%	62%	83%	71%
Women	26%	43%	77%	64%
Employment gap	18%	23%	9%	14%
In-labour force	44%	63%	84%	72%
Out-of-labour force	26%	41%	75%	58%

	2011, India	2014, India	2017, India	2017, World
Education gap	29%	21%	10%	23%
Secondary education or more	59%	64%	85%	77%
Primary education or less	31%	43%	75%	54%
Income gap	14%	15%	5%	13%
Richest 60%	41%	59%	82%	72%
Poorest 40%	27%	43%	77%	59%

Source: Reproduced from Derryl D'Silva, Zuzana Filkova, Frank Packer and Siddharth Tiwari, 'The design of digital financial infrastructure: lessons from India,' BIS Papers, No. 106, 15 December 2019, p. 13, available on https://www.bis.org/publ/bppdf/bispap106.htm

Research by Derryl D'Silva, Zuzana Filková, Frank Packer and Siddharth Tiwari for *BIS* showed how India had leapfrogged on financial inclusion matrices (Table 2.1). This shift occurred fundamentally because of what one of the report's authors called 'visionary action' by the State.[28]

Nehru to Modi: The Political Framing of JAM

The Modi government's first Economic Survey of 2014-15 came up with the acronym JAM—Jan Dhan, Aadhaar and mobile—as the three technologies that could radically transform the lives of the Indian poor. The regime bet its future on this combination of 'financial inclusion, biometric identification and digital access' as a means for revolutionary disruption.[29]

JAM is now so well known that it needs little explanation. Yet, few noticed that the term first appeared 'in a section [of the government's annual Economic Survey 2014-15] called "Wiping Every Tear from Every Eye"—the very evocative phrase from Pandit Nehru's "Tryst with Destiny" speech' as then chief economic advisor Arvind Subramanian later emphasised.[30] Nehru, in turn, had quoted Gandhi, and the Mahatma's ambition of wanting to 'wipe every tear from every eye' as a guiding principle for the country in his inaugural speech on 15 August 1947.

India's first prime minister is a lampoon figure for the Indian Right. He is blamed for many of the ills of modern India by the BJP. Yet, this delicious bipartisan congruence and the reference to Nehru's historic speech on the night of India's independence in 1947 further highlight the fact of how this uniquely Indian story of Aadhaar is also one of great continuity alongside great disruption.

The political framing was crucial. Subramanian recalls that the original chapter on JAM, which focused on the efficiency benefits and how replacing subsidies could reduce price distortions in the economy, 'could well have been written by a Washington Consensus-inspired economist, deserving today's damning sobriquet "neo-liberal"'.

When he showed it to Arun Jaitley, then finance minister, he reframed the document. 'Mr Jaitley asked for it to be reframed so as to better achieve equity objectives, highlight leakages under existing schemes and show how JAM could lead to better targeting so that poor beneficiaries are not excluded from the coverage of public programmes. The whole tone and tenor of the chapter changed and for the better. The subsequent spread of the term "JAM" owes in no small measure to the way that chapter was rewritten, thanks to his comments.'[31]

Why India Stack Mattered

All of this was possible because of what became known as 'India Stack'. As the IMF pointed out, this 'digital infrastructure known as the India Stack is revolutionizing access to finance'.[32] Aadhaar was central to its creation. In the software world, a 'stack' refers to multiple, interdependent layers of software services that are built on top of one another. It basically means a set of open application programming interfaces (API) and digital public goods that, like the building blocks of Lego, put together the blocks of identity, data and payments to take services to people on scale. In other words, India Stack is 'national plumbing for the Internet age'.

Essentially, this was 'foundational digital public infrastructure (DPI)' which consisted of 'unique digital identification, payments system and data exchange layer'. Broadly speaking, India Stack is the collective name of a set of shared digital building blocks, such as applications, systems and platforms powered by interoperable open standards or specifications. It consists of three different layers—unique identity (Aadhaar), payments systems (UPI, Aadhaar Payments Bridge, Aadhaar Enabled Payment Service) and data exchange (DigiLocker and Account Aggregator). 'Together they enable online, paperless, cashless and privacy-respecting digital access to a variety of public and private services.' As the IMF put it, 'India's foundational DPI, called India Stack, has been harnessed to foster innovation and competition, expand markets, close gaps in financial inclusion, boost government revenue collection and improve public expenditure efficiency. India's journey in developing a world-class DPI highlights powerful lessons for other countries embarking on their own digital transformation, in particular a design approach that focuses on shared building blocks.'[33]

By mid-2023, India was showcasing India Stack at the G-20 and making elements of it available to other countries. 'With India Stack, which was created in 2016, today you have a solution where you can create population scale solutions which are tested on platforms like payments, identity and healthcare,' says Ashwini Vaishnaw, minister for Railways, Communications and IT. 'Each of these are powerful in themselves. But together and combined they can help solve any major problem in the world. This is the power of India Stack and today the whole world wants to try out pieces of it.'[34]

At the base of the stack is an identity layer. This is powered by Aadhaar, which is linked to biometrics, as well as eKYC, which allows electronic authentication of a user's identity using Aadhaar and services like eSign for digital signatures. Above this is a payments layer. This includes systems like UPI, an instant real-time payments system (see chapter 5), an interoperable Aadhaar-enabled payment system (AePS) and an Aadhar Payments Bridge which enables the government to electronically channel benefits and subsidies to the bank accounts of beneficiaries.

Finally, at the top of these layers are services like DigiLocker that allow users to save authentic documents in a cloud and account aggregators that allow sharing of digital financial information between financial institutions with due consent from users (see Tables 2.2 and 2.3).

Table 2.2: India Stack: Digital Plumbing

Data Layer	Consent artefact	Digilocker	Account aggregator
Payment Layer	UPI	AEPS	Aadhaar payments bridge
Identity Layer	Aadhaar	eKYC	eSign

Source: Adapted from presentation by Ashwini Vaishnaw, minister for Railways, Communications and IT, 23 February 2023, ET Global India Summit.

By early 2023, at least seven countries had said they would sign up for using aspects of India Stack and India's digital public goods infrastructure.[35]

Undoubtedly, India's Aadhaar revolution is unique. No other country has built interconnected digital public infrastructure of this size. As Arvind Gupta and Philip E. Auerswald have pointed out, 'Aadhaar is both the only non-U.S. technical system globally to have broken the 1-billion-user threshold and the only such system to have been developed by the public sector. Due in part to its unique public-sector origins, Aadhaar has the distinction of having reached 1 billion users the fastest; the services built on Aadhaar, through the interoperability that defines the India Stack have, in turn, built their own record of scale and scope.'[36]

Table 2.3: Layers of India Stack

Name	Definition	Year of Launch	Operating Body
	Identity Layer		
Aadhaar	A twelve-digit unique identification number that is linked to biometric (fingerprints, iris, face), demographic (name, age, gender, address) and optional contact details (email, phone number)	2009	Unique Identification Authority of India (UIDAI)
eKYC	Electronic authentication of a customer's identity using their Aadhaar details	2013	Unique Identification Authority of India (UIDAI)
eSign	Service enabling Aadhaar holders to digitally and remotely sign documents with a legally valid electronic signature	2016	Controller of Certifying Authorities (CCA)
GSTN	A unique fifteen-digit identifier assigned to businesses and individuals who are registered under the Goods and Services Tax (GST) regime in India. It is used to track and manage the tax liabilities and compliance of registered taxpayers under the GST system	2017	The Goods and Services Tax Network (GSTN)
Udayam	A registration system for Micro, Small and Medium Enterprises (MSME) in India to make it easier for MSMEs to access government schemes and benefits	2020	The Ministry of Micro, Small and Medium Enterprises (MSME)

Name	Definition	Year of Launch	Operating Body
Payments Layer			
AePS (Aadhaar Enabled Payment System)	An interoperable financial system allowing customers to access and transact on their bank accounts by authenticating their Aadhaar	2010	National Payments Corporation of India (NPCI)
APB (Aadhaar Payment Bridge	System for electronically channeling government benefits and subsidies in the Aadhaar Enabled Bank Accounts (AEBA) of the intended beneficiaries	2011	National Payments Corporation of India (NPCI)
UPI	Unified Payments Interface is an instant real-time payment system	2016	National Payments Corporation of India (NPCI)
BBPS (Bharat Bill Payment System)	Integrated bill payment system providing a centralised platform for the payment of telephone bills, utility bills, etc.	2016	National Payments Corporation of India (NPCI)
Data Layer			
DigiLocker	Digitalisation service that provides an account in cloud to every Aadhaar holder to access authentic documents	2015	Ministry of Electronics and Information Technology (MeitY)

Name	Definition	Year of Launch	Operating Body
Account Aggregator	Enables consented access and sharing any person's digital financial information in a secure manner among financial institutions regulated by Financial Sector Regulators, namely, RBI, Securities and Exchange Board of India (SEBI), Insurance Regulatory and Development Authority of India (IRDAI), Pension Fund Regulatory and Development Authority (PFRDA)	2021	Reserve Bank of India (RBI)

Source: Reproduced from IMF, Cristian Alonso, Tanuj Bhojwani, Emine Hanedar, Dinar Prihardini, Gerardo Una and Kateryna Zhabska, 'Stacking up the Benefits: Lessons from India's Digital Journey,' IMF Working Papers, WP/23/78, p. 10, https://www.imf.org/en/Publications/WP/Issues/2023/03/31/Stacking-up-the-Benefits-Lessons-from-Indias-Digital-Journey-531692, p. 10.

Prime Minister Modi 'put digital transformation at the center of his plans' after winning power in 2014. 'For this reason, to the surprise of some, Modi not only backed the system developed by the previous government but also dramatically increased its funding, broadened its scope, and—most important—amplified its impact.'[37]

JAM emerged as a result of this, and has had profound implications on the nature of the Indian State, its relationship with poor citizens and social welfare spending. It is to this story we now turn.

3

THE PLAY
CREATING AN INDIAN WELFARE STATE 2.0

It takes just over 100 seconds. Lakshmi, a fifty-eight-year-old widow, shows her Aadhaar card at the government-authorised services centre in Keelara, a village in Mandya in southern Karnataka. She does not have a bank card or a passbook. But once her Aadhaar identification number is typed in and she presses her thumb on a scanner to verify her identity, the government-authorised agent across the counter can see on the computer screen that her precious monthly widow's pension of Rs 800 from a government Vidhwa Vetan (Widows Salary) scheme has hit her account.

She presses her thumb down again. This time to authorise a money transfer of Rs 800 from her account to the authorised agent's online DigiPay wallet. And he, like a virtual ATM machine, immediately hands over the amount in cash to her.

In less than two minutes, Lakshmi gets her full pension in hand. The agent, who works for a company authorised by the state government for such transactions at a government-authorised services centre, makes a small commission for the transaction from the government.

Lakshmi and the village in Mandya, with its mud houses nestled amid the green fields of the Old Mysuru region, about two hours from India's Silicon Valley in Bengaluru, encapsulate the massive changes that direct benefit transfers from the state have engendered for millions of poor Indians. Many of these changes are invisible to people like us in the middle classes. Yet, they constitute a seismic shift in Indian society.

Most of these changes are the consequence of the digital transformation of the State and its delivery mechanism for the poor over the past decade. In important ways, this has changed the nature of the State itself, as well as its relationship with some of its poorest citizens.

Lakshmi did not have a bank account five years ago. It was opened after she got an Aadhaar card in 2018. 'I have been getting my pension with this Aadhaar card,' she told me in Kannada. Her son, who works as a driver in Bengaluru, explains that his mother's pension comes through her Bank of Baroda account. Earlier, she had to travel far from her village to get her pension. Now 'it has become easier with this', she says.[1]

Lakshmi benefited from the DigiPay system, jointly launched by the Common Services Centre (CSC), e-Governance Services India Limited and National Payments Corporation of India (NPCI) in January 2016.[2] Using Aadhaar authentication, this payments system is interoperable across all banks and facilitates disbursements of Central and state government welfare schemes like MGNREGA, social security pensions, handicapped and old age pensions.

'DigiPay uses your fingerprint, biometrics and account number linked with Aadhaar. You put in the Aadhaar number, bank name and mobile number, and we can transfer the money you are entitled to through the DigiPay app to ourselves. And we pay you the cash,' explains Rupesh Kumar, a government-authorised CSC agent in Dehradun's Jhajhra.[3]

CSCs are physical facilities for delivering government e-services to citizens who may not otherwise have access to internet connectivity, and saves them multiple visits to government offices. India had 5,23,208 active CSCs by March 2023, of which 4,15,228 were at the gram panchayat (village council) level. Almost 80 per cent of these were in rural areas.[4]

'The main difference is that while using e-wallets like PayTM, the money is transferred to a person's e-wallet,' said Kumar. 'Here, it is transferred to their main account by the government. From there it comes to us, and after their authorisation we provide them the cash. You don't have to go to a bank or ATM. You can get your cash directly from us with your fingerprint or biometrics, and the system works.'

Lakshmi's pension was just one of the 860.62 lakh DigiPay transactions that took place at government-authorised centres in India in 2020-21. These transactions were worth Rs 10,541 crore. In a COVID-affected year, this was over 300 per cent more than in the previous year.[5]

In Lakshmi's state of Karnataka itself, the number of centres registered for such DigiPay transactions more than doubled between 2019-20 and 2020-21 (from 5,003 to 10,677). The number of such transactions (from 1.43 lakh crore transactions to 11.1 lakh crore) and their cash value (from Rs 18.17 lakh crore to Rs 130 crore) also went up by over seven times.[6]

The Indian State has always spent large amounts of money on welfare for the poor. But it has struggled to identify the right beneficiaries. Large chunks of the money meant for the poor would get siphoned off in transit at various levels by a corruption-ridden bureaucracy. Moreover, millions of Indians, like Lakshmi, struggled to even identify themselves to the State.

That many of these millions of poor Indians, in a country with such sharp demographic, social and cultural divides, can now receive their full welfare entitlements virtually at the click of a digital button sounded like utopian science fiction even a decade ago. When the first such experiments with DBT for Central government schemes started in the last years of the Manmohan Singh-led UPA government, few believed they would eventually lead to a transformation that would retool the very architecture of the Indian State's relationship with the poor. Many problems remain, of course, and no system is perfect. Yet, there is no question that there has been a paradigm shift. For example, Lakshmi's own district of Mandya was among the first wave of half a dozen districts in Karnataka where electronic benefit transfer (EBT) pilot projects were first implemented for government schemes, in a push by the Reserve Bank of India between 2010 and 2013.[7]

Decoding Modi and India's Direct Benefit Transfers Ramp-up

The Narendra Modi government inherited an incipient structure for DBT in 2014. During Manmohan Singh's UPA, it had undergone a testing phase with several schemes. This was done using the back-end tech stack that had been created and built on with Aadhaar.

Modi, from July 2014 onwards, gave the initiative his full political backing and scaled it up massively. The figures tell the story of the shift:

- Schemes@11x: The new government doubled down on DBTs and expanded it eleven-fold, from twenty-eight government schemes in 2013-14 to 312 in 2022-23. At one point, as many as 437 schemes were within the ambit of DBT.[8]
- People@8x: Government data shows that the initial 10.8 crore beneficiaries of DBT reported in 2013-14 (many of whom were added under UPA) went up by over eight times to 92.3 crore beneficiaries by 2022-23.
- Money@110x: Actual direct cash payments into people's bank accounts went up by over thirty-four times from Rs 7,367 crore in 2013-14 to Rs 2.55 lakh crore in 2022-23. If you add transfers in kind (such as food grains under the public distribution system), then total transfers went up by more than a whopping 110 times in the same period (see Table 3.1).

Table 3.1: DBT Transfers Grew at a Fast Pace in Modi-led NDA 1 and 2: DBT Transfers (2013–14 to 2019–20)

Year	Schemes (No.)	Beneficiaries, Cash (No. in crore)	Beneficiaries, in Kind (No. in crore)	DBT, in Cash (Rs in crore)	DBT, in Kind (Rs in crore)	DBT, Total (Rs in crore)
2013–14	28	10.8		7,367.7	-	7,367.7
2014–15	34	22.8		38,926.2	-	38,926.2
2015–16	59	31.2		61,942.4	-	61,942.2
2016–17	142	35.7		74,689.4	-	74,689.4
2017–18	437	46.3	77.7	1,70,292.2	20,578.7	1,90,870.9
2018–19	434	59	76.3	2,14,092	1,15,704.3	3,29,796.3
2019–20	426	71.4	72.2	2,39,729.4	1,41,902.12	3,81,631.5
2020–21	316	98.7	81.2	29,6,577.6	2,55,949.6	5,52,527.2
2021–22	313	74.8	104.1	2,68,139.09	3,62,125.63	6,30,264.72
2022–23	312	71	93.4	2,55,539.25	5,57,748.49	8,13,287.74
Total						30,82,303.86

Source: Collated by the author from Minister of State for Finance Anurag Singh Thakur, Answer to Lok Sabha Unstarred Question No. 1183, 19 September 2020; Minister of State for Finance P. Radhakrishnan, Answer to Lok Sabha Unstarred Question No. 2827, 28 December 2018;[9] Cash and kind break-up of total schemes, beneficiaries and spending from 2017–18 onwards is from DBT Mission, Government of India, https://dbtbharat.gov.in/.

Look deeper at the numbers and three major changes are inherent.

First, the nature of DBT itself changed. Initially, DBT started with and was largely focused on rural unemployment, with MGNREGA, a social security legislation which became law in 2005. It aimed to provide the 'right to work' in rural areas by guaranteeing at least 100 days of work per year to one member of any household who volunteered for unskilled manual work.

About halfway through Modi's first tenure as prime minister, in 2016, half of the DBT payments by the Central government were MGNREGS-related. The flagship scheme of the Manmohan Singh-led UPA government had come into force in February 2006, following legislation in 2005. Interestingly, by 2021, the weightage of the guaranteed employment scheme in the government's DBT payments had gone down drastically. Much less is spent on MGNREGA now: as a percentage of DBT, it went from over 51 per cent in 2014 to 11.6 per cent by 2022.

Crucially, only the share of MGNREGA as a percentage of DBT went down during these years. Not the absolute spend, until 2022. In fact, actual spending on the rural employment guarantee scheme went up by over 50 per cent between 2019 and 2021, from Rs 46,046.1 crore to Rs 73,551.1 crore (see Figure 3.1). The change in percentage is because the Central government had started spending much more on other welfare categories.[10]

By 2021, over one-third (34.4 per cent) of DBT payments were focused on the PDS for food security. The second highest category was fertilisers (19.6 per cent) and MNREGS came in third (see Figure 3.1). Taken together, food and fertilisers (in kind), accounted for 54 per cent of all DBT expenditure by 2021, up from barely 5 per cent in 2017.

Second, the charts in Figure 3.1 show how the State's focus, from 2014 onwards, shifted significantly to creating an expanded social welfare net for poor citizens. This gave birth to a new political

Figure 3.1: India's Welfare State 2.0 has Changed Character: Scaling Up and Change

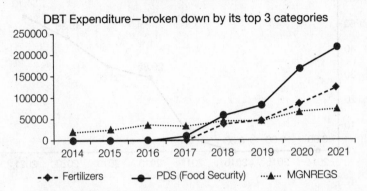

DBT Expenditure—broken down by its top 3 categories

- -◆- Fertilizers ●— PDS (Food Security) ···▲··· MGNREGS

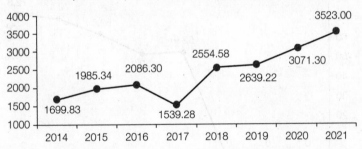

DBT Expenditure per capita has been going up continually

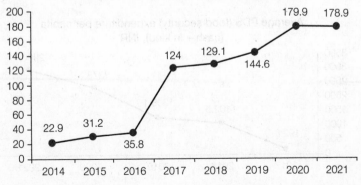

Number of DBT beneficiaries (all schemes), Crore

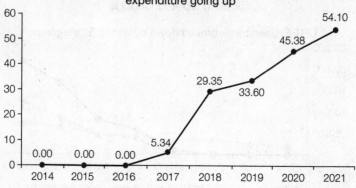

Food and Fertiliser expenditure (in kind) as % of total DBT expenditure going up

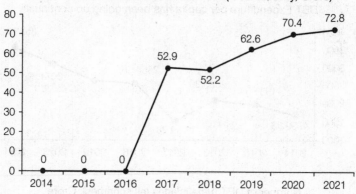

Number of DBT beneficiaries for PDS (food security, Crore)

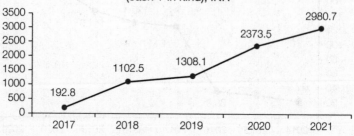

Average PDS (food security) expenditure per capita (cash + in kind), INR

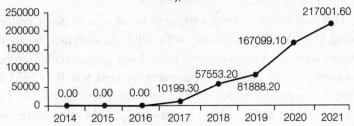

Total DBT expenditure on PDS (food security—in kind), Crore

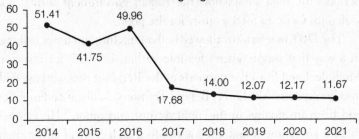

MNREGS expenditure as % of total DBT spending has been going down

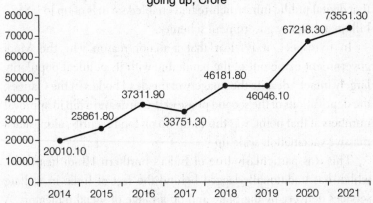

DBT expenditure on MNREGS has been going up, Crore

Source: Analysis by Rishabh Srivastava, defog.ai and Data Narratives.ai, with Nalin Mehta, Datashastra, https://datanarratives.com/dashboard/?id=f0cff01f-0a82-4ef6-ae2d-2d5bf6794cda. Data from DBT Mission, 2023.

terminology: 'labharthees' (beneficiaries), which too had profound implications for politics.[11]

This modern safety net for the poor became particularly visible during the COVID pandemic, with DBT expenditures on food security increasing by over three times from pre-pandemic levels. Consider this: In 2018, PDS spending in kind was Rs 57,553.2 crore. It ramped up to Rs 81,888.2 crore in 2019, Rs 167,099.14 crore in 2020 and Rs 217,001.6 crore in 2021. In other words, it almost quadrupled.[12] While there were gaps—most notably the case of migrant labourers moving from state to state during the lockdown period—the data shows how the Indian government shifted and scaled up focus on food security for the poor.

The DBT mechanism allowed better targeting and lesser leakages in a way that simply wasn't feasible earlier. In 2022, for instance, Modi declared from the ramparts of the Red Fort that working with 'modern systems like Direct Benefit Transfers, Aadhaar and mobiles' had been invaluable in the 'fight against corruption'. He claimed that his government had saved about Rs 2 lakh crore of government welfare spending which used to 'go into the wrong hands' through such means.[13] By 2023, the government's revenue secretary declared that digital public infrastructure had enabled savings of up to US$27 billion across key government schemes.[14]

In retrospect, it is clear that a major reason why the Modi government came out of the pandemic with its political popularity largely intact[15] despite the imagery of the dead bodies in the Ganges, the deprivations of the second phase of the virus and a dip in approval numbers at that point, was this ramp-up on food security, alongside a massive vaccination scale-up.[16]

This was particularly true of India's northern Hindi heartland, which has traditionally lagged behind the rest of India in welfare services delivery by the State and on a range of social indicators. A case in point is the Uttar Pradesh elections of March 2022, which closely followed the second wave of the pandemic. Not only did Chief Minister Yogi Adityanath retain power in India's most populous and politically significant state, he won an absolute majority (255 of 403 seats for the BJP) and an increased vote share (41.3 per cent). This was also the first time in thirty-seven years that an incumbent party was returned to power in Lucknow.

That the Bharatiya Janata Party (BJP) could pull off this electoral feat after two years of economic strife (the Gross Domestic Product had just returned at the time to its pre-lockdown size), the miseries of the coronavirus lockdowns and a vociferous farmers' agitation accrue in large measure to the shifts in India's political economy that were engendered by DBT. This is a big claim to make, of course. I have attempted to detail how this unfolded separately, in Chapter 4, along with the mechanisms of political mobilisation that accompanied it.[17]

In December 2022, the BJP also won its greatest ever victory in Gujarat, winning 156 of 182 seats with 53 per cent vote share, although it failed to retain power in Himachal Pradesh, where the Congress returned to office.[18] For context, Gujarat is a state where the BJP has not lost power since the 1990s, while in Himachal power has historically alternated between the BJP and the Congress in each state election cycle.

People vote for multiple reasons, of course. Politics rarely follows a unidimensional matrix for most non-ideological voters. Also, both Gujarat and Uttar Pradesh have a very different polity—socially, economically and culturally—and were very different contests. What is common is that both states were among the worst hit by the pandemic. They also saw some of the worst tragedies on the ground.

The point is that the increased social welfare net of the state (see Figures 3.1 and 3.2), enabled by DBT, played a big role in mitigating the negative political impact of the pandemic. Travelling across UP in early 2022, for example, I heard a constant refrain in rural areas about 'ration and tel [oil]'.

It would be too simplistic to reduce an election contest to just one issue. Beyond ideology, other factors like leadership, social and caste matrices, party organisation, etc. have to come together for a poll victory. For example, Himachal Pradesh, which normally oscillates between the BJP and the Congress, saw the BJP losing power in 2022. The opposition Congress, in May 2023, also wrested power back from the BJP in Karnataka—another state which has not voted back an incumbent government since 1985—ironically, by using several DBT-focused promises.[19]

The point is that these electoral contests played out within a new context. They occurred at a time when there had been a massive expansion of the social welfare net (see Figures 3.1 and 3.2) which retooled the Indian State's delivery mechanisms for the poor on a scale that hadn't been seen since Independence. That the BJP was the ruling party on whose watch these changes occurred helped the party to gain political mileage. This ensured that the BJP did not pay a political price for the pandemic in the way that it might otherwise have. In other words, changing the DNA of the State's relationship with the poor through DBT provided the BJP with a massive political safety net.

Finally, it is not just the spread of the coverage that has increased with more beneficiaries. It is also what goes into the pocket of each labharthee.

In 2014, average direct beneficiary transfers per capita amounted to Rs 1,699.3. By 2016, this had increased to Rs 2,086.2. By 2020, the year of the COVID lockdowns, it had almost doubled to Rs 3,071.3 per Indian, hitting Rs 3,522.1 in 2021. DBT expenditure per capita has also been going up continuously. To be clear, these are pan-India numbers, reflecting schemes run by the Central government, many of which are run together with state governments, both BJP and non-BJP. The rise in the spending shows how the DBT net has expanded.

This is why Modi could declare to an audience of corporate CEOs in 2023 that his government had transferred a cumulative amount of Rs 28 lakh crore into the pockets of the poor since it came to power. As he put it:

The example of Direct Benefit Transfers, you must have noted this for sure. You know that in our country, corruption, leakages and middlemen were commonplace in government schemes and the society had accepted this also. Government budgets and government spending kept increasing but poverty also kept increasing. Four decades ago, the then Prime Minister Rajiv Gandhi had said that if Delhi sends Rs 1 on welfare, it becomes just 15 paise by the time it reaches the beneficiary. Which palms got greased, I don't know.

Our government has so far spent Rs 28 lakh crore through various schemes. Now think what Rajiv Gandhi said. If I add his Rs 15 paise out of Rs 1 for today, then at 85 per cent, Rs 24 lakh crore would have gone into somebody's pockets. Somebody would have looted it. It would have disappeared. And only Rs 4 lakh crore would have reached the poor. But because I reimagined, the DBT system was given importance. Today if Rs 1 leaves Delhi, 100 of our 100 paise reaches the poor.[20]

In many ways, it is this political framing that is at the heart of the big shift in India's politics since 2014.

Many opponents of the BJP think that the party is a one-trick pony, focused only on Hindutva, cultural battles and Hindu nationalism. But the numbers show that a tech-enabled paradigm shift in India's political economy with DBT formed the bedrock of Modi's continuing political dominance between 2014 and 2023. While the BJP, after 2014, has been unapologetic about Hindutva, DBT and the political outreach around it to the labharthee class has been a crucial bulwark of the new BJP model.

How India Broke the Digital Barrier: Common Service Centres in the Villages

Two-and-a-half thousand kilometres up north from Mandya, I met Neeraj Singh in the hill town of Almora, set amid pine trees and oak forests in the Kumaon hills of Uttarakhand. Neeraj's story exemplified the story of Digital India. And hearing it, I finally understood how India had broken through the digital divide to achieve the scale it has.

A postgraduate diploma holder in computer science, Neeraj runs a CSC in Almora's Basoli Takula village. After finishing his education, he decided to stay back in the village, unlike most others of his generation who left for distant cities in the plains to find jobs.

The hills didn't have jobs, but Neeraj stayed back because, just as he was graduating, the Aadhaar wave came to his village. The agency in charge of setting up Aadhaar cards, UIDAI, was hiring agents across India to convince people to register for the cards. Somebody in Neeraj's village won a contract to organise government camps for Aadhaar registration. Neeraj initially got a job as an agent doing this. It was 2013, Manmohan Singh was prime minister, and Nandan Nilekani had just set up the agency.

Neeraj says he used to do 70–80 Aadhaar registrations on average and made about Rs 150 per day. Six months into his work as an agent for Aadhaar, the agency took out a new tender for hiring registration agents in his district. Neeraj, who had learned the job by now, applied and won the tender for Balasore district. He was now in charge of all registrations in the area and set up a ten-member team for Aadhaar sign-ups. As an agent, he had made a small commission for every card he registered. Now, as district in-charge, he made a commission of Rs 18 for each person his team enrolled.

Neeraj told me the job allowed him to stay back in the comfort of his village. It empowered him not to undertake the arduous journey of immigration, like many of his friends had. As India built the foundation of its digital techade with its unique ID revolution, it was foot soldiers like Neeraj who made the transformation possible.

Neeraj's problem was that, by 2015, the Aadhaar wave had begun to subside. Once almost everyone he knew had one, what would remain of his job? Neeraj began to worry. Then came a new career opportunity, which followed from the Aadhaar cascade.

Back in 2014, the Modi government's Digital India initiative had sounded like just another grandiose political announcement. For Neeraj in Almora, it opened up a new career.

The Modi government focused on increasing CSCs in India, just as the previous government had seeded Aadhaar registrations. In 2015, Neeraj applied for, and won, another government contract. This time to set up a CSC.

The CSC contract for Neeraj in the Kumaon hills was the outcome of a larger decision taken in Delhi. The new Central government was pushing for the creation of millions of new bank accounts and moving welfare schemes to DBT. People may have had mobile phones and data, but most still found it impossible to deal with sarkari systems, including digital ones. Just uploading documents, for example, to get an ID registered, needed a very specific kind of digital literacy. CSCs were designed as a solution to this problem, as places where villagers could go to manage their digital engagements with the faceless mai-baap sarkar. They were the critical backbone of the digital shift.

In Basoli in 2015, for example, people from Neeraj's village had to travel 30–35 kilometres to the district headquarters to get any government document verified. Neeraj's CSC now provided vital services in the village itself. A list of some of these services is instructive. It provides insights into the requirements for villagers in their daily interaction with the government to access their dues:

- Life certificate
- Revenue documents
- Character certificate
- Caste certificate
- Life insurance policies issued by the Life Insurance Corporation of India
- PM Kisan payments (for farmers)
- Ayushman Bharat (health payments)
- MNREGS cards

- Jan Dhan accounts
- Photocopies and uploading of government documents

In the initial years, Neeraj says his small village centre opened up about 10,000 PM Kisan accounts for the Kisan Samman Nidhi, about 40,000–50,000 Ayushman Bharat cards for medical insurance, 3,000–4,000 Shram cards and a large number of MNREGS cards.

Table 3.2: CSCs in Villages Powered India's Digital Shift

List of Services offered through CSCs			
S. No.	Contents	S. No.	Contents
I	**Aadhaar Services**	5	**Educational Services**
1.1	Aadhaar Services: Generation of Aadhaar	5.1	Education Services: Digital Literacy
1.2	Aadhaar Services: E-KYC & Authentication	5.2	Various online courses of NIELIT & NIOS. various courses of IGNOU, IITs, Private Universities
1.3	Aadhaar Services: Aadhaar Printing	5.3	Various courses of CSC Academy
1.4	Aadhaar Updates (UCL)	6	**Legal Services**
2	**Central G2C Services PM Welfare Schemes**	6.1	Tele-legal Consultation Services
2.1	Ayushman Bharat Yojana	6.2	E-Courts Services
2.2	PM Fasal Bima Yojana	7	**Financial Inclusion Services**
2.3	PM Ujjwala Scheme (LPG Booking)	7.1	Financial Inclusion: Banking Services
2.4	PM Shram Yogi Maan-dhan Yojana	7.2	Financial Inclusion: DigiPay (AEPS)
2.5	PM Kisan Maan-dhan Yojana	7.3	Financial Inclusion: Insurance Services

S. No.	Contents	S. No.	Contents
4.2	PDS Services	11.1	Grameen E-Store
4.3	Labour Registration Services	11.2	Other Services: Products Distribution
4.4	E-Stamp	11.3	Other Services: Agriculture Services
4.5	E-Vahan: Sarathi Transport Services	11.4	Other Services: Mobile/ DTH Recharge
4.6	Himachal Swasthya Bima Yojana (HIMCARE)	11.5	Other Services: IT Return Filing
4.7	Other State G2C Services: Recruitment Services	11.6	Other Services: Diginame
4.8	Other State G2C Services: Municipal Services	12	**Skill Development**
4.9	Other State G2C Services: Swastha Bima	12.1	Skill Development: Schemes and Courses
4.1	Other State G2C Services: Fasal Bima Yojana	12.2	Skill Development: Job Portals

Source: Government of India, Ministry of Electronics and Information Technology, in Lok Sabha Unstarred Question No. 4448, 30 March 2022. Answered by Minister of State for Electronics and Information Technology Rajeev Chandrasekhar.[21]

When the Modi government pushed for Jan Dhan accounts, several banks held camps in Neeraj's village. He says a major reason why people 'lined up to open the accounts' was that 'Modiji had said money will come' if you opened one.

CSCs emerged as a vital last-mile link to connect the plans made in Delhi with those they were intended for. This worked on the ground because the people running them earned a commission for each service they offered. For each new bank account that a

CSC worker enabled, they earned 2 per cent commission from the bank. Similarly, most schemes needed verified photocopies of the beneficiary's documents to be uploaded onto government registration sites before they could be activated. The CSC also earned a small fee from customers for some of these services, as well as 1–2 per cent commission for each verified transaction for some schemes.

Digital Assistants: CSC 2.0

In the time of ChatGPT and digital assistants, it is easy to get carried away. The truth is that the idea of digital services may look seductive on PowerPoint presentations or in the tech-talk of Silicon Valley, but in the real world of the poor, such gung-ho schemes often fall flat. Mainly because the loops are not closed on the ground. In that sense, CSCs were a game-changing innovation, working as a kind of digital assistant for the poor to access government schemes.

The thought behind it, as a senior bureaucrat told me, was that 'there should be a suitable infrastructure to give them suitable assistant service delivery and digital service delivery. Somebody should be available in his village to guide them and to provide him that service. So that's how the idea of a Common Services Centre was pushed.'[22]

The idea had been around since 2008. By 2014, India had 80,000 such centres. Just as with its DBT push, the government doubled down and initiated what it called CSC 2.0 from 2015 onwards. The result was that by December 2022, the CSCs were scaled up by almost seven times, to 5,49,000.[23] India has 2.5 lakh gram panchayats. The idea was to put at least one CSC in every one of them.[24]

'The push came from the top that this is one of the key programmes and we have to make it a success,' says Saurabh Kumar. 'So, you know, the whole machinery of the government geared up accordingly.' As private secretary to the then IT minister Ravi Shankar Prasad, Kumar had a ringside view of how the shift happened.

'By now, almost every panchayat—not all—has a service centre,' he told me in mid-2022. 'These are digital delivery service kiosks where anybody can go and avail services—like banking services, like DBT or state government services, like electricity bill payment *karna hai*, mobile recharge *karaana hai*,' said the bureaucrat. 'These kinds of services, and a lot of them. You get it all at one kiosk only. For example, vaccination is happening. You don't have a smartphone. You can go there and get it if you don't have a smartphone. This system or network of Common Service Centres played a vital role in ensuring that nobody is left out.'

By February 2022, 84 per cent of CSCs created nationwide were at the gram panchayat level (see Table 3.3).

Table 3.3: CSCs Became the Backbone of
Digital Service Delivery

State/Union Territory-wise roll out of CSCs, as on 28 February 2022		
State/UT	*Functional CSCs (Urban+Rural)*	*Functional CSCs at GP level*
Andhra Pradesh	8,960	6,639
Arunachal Pradesh	144	103
Assam	9,852	8,983
Bihar	47,755	42,626
Chhattisgarh	18,238	14,535
Goa	143	94
Gujarat	12,337	8,466
Haryana	19,370	13,614
Himachal Pradesh	4,879	4,288
Jharkhand	18,206	15,559
Karnataka	11,023	7,352
Kerala	6,144	4,772
Madhya Pradesh	39,828	30,033
Maharashtra	46,716	35,848

State/UT	Functional CSCs (Urban+Rural)	Functional CSCs at GP level
Manipur	953	788
Meghalaya	882	775
Mizoram	337	235
Nagaland	506	351
Odisha	14,715	12,795
Punjab	10,829	7,523
Rajasthan	20,052	16,187
Sikkim	72	56
Tamil Nadu	11,091	7,317
Telangana	5,775	3,933
Tripura	1,621	1,391
Uttar Pradesh	1,12,276	88,451
Uttarakhand	8,413	6,143
West Bengal	20,921	18,802
State Total	**4,52,038**	**3,57,659**
Andaman & Nicobar	50	29
Chandigarh	132	6
Dadra & NH. D&D	75	50
Delhi	4,159	228
Jammu & Kashmir	6,927	5,694
Ladakh	109	98
Lakshadweep	12	12
Puducherry	203	111
UT Total	**11,667**	**6,228**
Grand Total	**4,63,705**	**3,63,887**

Source: Rajeev Chandrasekhar, minister of state for Electronics and Information Technology, response in Government of India, Ministry of Electronics and Information Technology, Lok Sabha Unstarred Question No. 4448. Answered on: 30 March 2022, 'CSC for Cyber Services'. chrome-extension://efaidnbmnnnibpcajpcglclefindmkaj/http://164.100. 24.220/loksabhaquestions/annex/178/AU4448.pdf

The Basoli village CSC in Almora also exemplifies how things changed. When it opened in 2015, Neeraj's CSC was the first one in his area. It serviced twenty-six villages at the time. By 2022, the district had as many as five centres.

'On average, twenty to forty people come in every day,' Neeraj told me. This was in sharp contrast to the early years of the scale-up. Back then, he says, 'There was such a rush to get registered that I didn't even get the time to eat food. There were so many people that I didn't have time to take a lunch break on most days.'[25]

The CSCs, which offer a large bouquet of e-services on a single platform, basically work as localised help-desk support. Many also serve as a hub for what the government calls village-level entrepreneurs (VLE). These are people who deliver government schemes and non-government schemes at the centres. For the most part, they own the centres and earn a commission on each transaction they make.[26] By 2023, India had a network of 5.4 lakh such VLEs, 4.3 lakh at the gram panchayat level.[27]

'Basically, you get all government services in one place in a CSC,' explained Jitendra Sachdeva, who runs a centre in Dehradun's Premnagar. 'For filling every form, there are different procedures. It is our job to keep getting ourselves updated and we have all the relevant software. We are basically digital assistants. To apply for any government scheme, the government gives detailed guidelines. Ninety per cent people don't know them. Many documents need to be uploaded, in specific formats, and they can often make a mistake. So their applications get rejected. We know the system, so we can ensure that doesn't happen.'[28]

Aspiring agents have to take specific examinations to qualify to run CSCs. The exams focus on the kind of documents that are needed for different schemes. For example, as Neeraj explains, there are 'fourteen modules on documents for various schemes in the entrance exam itself, as well as on software'. Essentially, the agents at CSCs can only offer the services they are qualified for, not all. Their incentive is commissions. They also offer private services like insurance schemes through private banks, and photocopying, which applicants often avail of. Agenting for such private services helps shore up the income the agents make.

'A Page from the Indian Book': Digital Public Goods

The numbers explain why the Indian experiment with digital public goods is being watched so carefully by big tech giants and policymakers around the world. By 2023, Google and Alphabet CEO Sundar Pichai, Microsoft CEO Satya Nadella, Microsoft's founder and philanthropist Bill Gates, the IMF and the World Bank, had all weighed in on the implications of the Indian scale-up of tech solutions for developmental problems and inclusivity.

On a visit to Delhi, Pichai emphasised that 'what India has accomplished with the UPI, Aadhaar and the payments stack' showcases 'the value of having an open, connected stack that works'. He said, 'India can be a shining example.'[29]

Similarly, Nadella termed the 'magic of India Stack' and how the technology stack co-evolved with government policies and yojanas as 'a virtuous cycle that is unlike anything I have seen'. Speaking at a conference in Bengaluru, he rated it as 'perhaps the greatest contribution that India can make to the world'.

> Think about it. The idea that there is a digital public good is great. But that there is a digital public good … that there are new ways to use this, to make it possible for every society and economy to be more inclusive is what I learn in India every time I come …
>
> For the common man to be able to use the greatest technology and do something that is useful to them. It is not about tech for tech's stake. That to me is what I think India can contribute. The age of celebration of technology for technology's sake is over. It is about really thinking about technology and its use for everyone in the world. And that I think is India's greatest contribution.[30]

His comments foreshadowed Bill Gates's observation at a lecture in Delhi that India's digital public infrastructure, Aadhaar and financial empowerment enabled '80 per cent of Indians to be covered by bank accounts in less than a decade, a feat that may have taken 47 years by traditional methods. Many elements of this digital infrastructure are now being imported to other countries too.' As he put it, 'India is not just a beneficiary of new breakthroughs, but an innovator of them.'[31]

The IMF went a step further, terming the Indian DBT scheme a 'logistical marvel'.[32] Its managing director, Kristilina Georgiva, says that, during the COVID crisis, while India may have had less money than others, it had an 'advantage' in creating a safety net because 'it was well targeted because of digitisation'. India, she said:

built an incredibly agile foundation for a time of shock through digital ID and digital public infrastructure. That is the biggest advantage India had at the outset of COVID. I hope that during the G20 all countries take a page from the Indian book for themselves.[33]

Speaking at the IMF and World Bank Group's annual meeting in Washington in 2022, Paulo Mauro, the IMF's deputy director of Fiscal Affairs, explained:

If I look at the case of India, it is actually quite impressive. In fact, just because of the sheer size of the country, it is a logistical marvel how these programmes that seek to help people who are at low income levels reach literally hundreds of millions of people ...

Perhaps the interesting part is that in these examples there is a lot of technological innovation. In the case of India, one thing that is striking is the use of the unique identification system, the Aadhaar ... So being somewhat innovative in identifying people, in processing their applications for transfers through digital means, deploying funds through ... mobile banking. This is something that countries can learn from each other.[34]

It is interesting to note that, Germany, for example, takes eighteen months to match bank and tax IDs and the state's tech back-end can handle only about 100,000 transfers a day. When *The Economist*'s European economics editor mentioned this on Twitter,[35] his tweet quickly went viral. Many of the leading lights of India Stack responded with comparisons to the Indian system. Pramod Varma, who is counted as one of the architects of Aadhaar and UPI, pointed out that the Indian direct cash transfer system was very advanced, interoperable across all banks, fully digital, low-cost and covered more than 650 million people.

The politicians jumped into the fray too. As the junior IT minister smugly wrote on Twitter, '... meanwhile, India uses technology to drive digital payments and speedy delivery of government subsidies/benefits to all citizens'.[36]

The political response reflected just how central DBT had become to Indian politics and its political economy. Equally, it was now part of India's soft power too, and a crucial lever of its showcasing in global fora in the year of its G20 presidency.

4

IMPACT
DIGITAL WELFARE 2.0 AND HOW IT WORKS

'I have been gram pradhan for five years and got about Rs 40 lakh in this time period to spend on the village,' Hemant Chauhan told us, sitting by the ancient Shakumbhari Devi temple near Saharanpur in western UP. 'In comparison to that, we have seen about Rs 2 crore each coming in yearly into the village through just two schemes: personal toilets under Swachh Bharat and money for houses under PM Awas Yojana-Gramin (PMAY-G).'

Chauhan holds an MBA degree and used to work for Johnson & Johnson as a marketing executive in Lucknow and Dehradun before he decided to move back to the Shahpur Bans Must village in Behat tehsil in 2013. Because he was well educated, the villagers decided to elect him as the pradhan, a position that allowed Chauhan to play a vital role in the management and administration of a plethora of government schemes that touched the life of the village.

We were chatting about these schemes in June 2020, discussing whether things were really different under the Modi government as compared to Manmohan Singh's time, when he startled me with the stark comparison on governmental spending in his area.

So, was the size and scale of the welfare money the big political differentiator? Did previous governments not spend similar amounts on these schemes? Indeed, was not the toilets scheme simply a renamed, repackaged mega-version of Manmohan Singh's Nirmal Bharat Scheme, rechristened Swachh Bharat? Just like the PMAY-G was a reworked version of what was once called the Indira Awas Yojana?

Sure, he answered, but 'you people don't understand the real difference'. After Modi came to power, the money for these schemes 'comes directly into the labharthee's bank account, whether for toilets or for houses'. A villager wanting to get a toilet made, if eligible under Swachh Bharat, gets Rs 12,000,[1] while those under the poverty line wanting a pucca house under PMAY-G get Rs 1,20,000 in their bank account.[2] 'Imagine, if they got Rs 12,000 for fixing a toilet but it cost only Rs 5,000 to do it,' Chauhan said sardonically. 'The rest of the money is theirs.' The discussion had clearly hit a raw nerve.

'What if they just got some plastering done and got their name written on the list? Whether a toilet is made or not made, the money is with the labharthee. It's the same thing with the houses. People are getting a moti rakam [fat amount], Rs 1,20,000, to build a house. So much money may not be required.'[3]

His heart seemed to be in the right place, but the pradhan was clearly not thrilled by the DBTs flowing into villagers' bank accounts. Yet, his micro-perspective had nailed the radical shift that such transfers had caused in the political economy of his village. Earlier, villagers had to go with their 'arms outstretched' ('haath phaila ke') before local officials to get their entitlements, often for a large cut.[4] Now, the money came directly into their accounts. The officials could still demand a cut in return for sanctioning the payment, or if the villager wanted to be approved as a beneficiary for other schemes. But the fact that the money first reached the beneficiary increased his bargaining power. DBTs, for all the faults in the system, drastically shifted the power dynamics in the village.

Money had gone into bank accounts earlier too, but wily village pradhans would make fake job cards for schemes like the MGNREGS—say, fifty fake ones in a village of 200. Once Aadhaar cards were linked to bank accounts, this became much more difficult. Of course, leakages, corruption and systemic inefficiencies still remained, as a range of studies have documented.[5] Yet, from the villagers' point of view, the scope for pilferage was reduced.

'You cannot move Rs 2 from here to there,' a long-time observer of such schemes in Lucknow told us. 'They have made their system so strong that through the government the money goes directly into people's accounts—if it is Rs 200, Rs 200 reaches. The mentality has been that if it was Rs 2,000 earlier, then only Rs 200 would reach the village. So, people think that this guy has brought magic.'[6]

Direct Benefit Transfers: Origins and Ramp-up

The village in Saharanpur exemplified the sea change in the rural welfare economy that DBT had wrought. Equally, it was an example of how an idea pushed through by Manmohan Singh at the fag end of UPA-2 was scaled up and appropriated by the Modi government.

The DBT programme was formally launched with much fanfare by the UPA-2 government on 1 January 2013. Then Rural Affairs minister Jairam Ramesh even coined a political slogan for it: 'Aapka Paisa, Aap Ke Haath' (Your Money in Your Hands).

It was launched after months of internal sparring among Congress ministers on the usage of Aadhaar. Once the objections were overcome, however, it was hailed at the time as the 'world's largest cash-transfer scheme'. The political potential of it was clear even then. One observer saw it as the 'most historic one-shot transformative social policy instrument in India', 'on a par with the abolition of the zamindari system, the Green Revolution, banks nationalisation, the Right to Information and the National Rural Employment Guarantee Scheme'.[7]

Political editors covering the BJP and the Congress noted at the time that the launch of the scheme had brought the 'spring back into the step of Congress leaders'[8] after months of being on the defensive as they headed into an election year. The UPA initially launched

DBT on a trial basis for twenty-four Union government schemes in forty-three districts.[9] The first trials took place in Rajasthan and then in Andhra Pradesh, but it took a few months for the teething problems to be overcome. The DBT trials were, in fact, ushered in by the Congress a few months before even the banking system moved to accepting Aadhaar numbers for paperless KYC verification through UIDAI in September 2013.[10] However, initial feedback on the early experiments was not great. By the time many of the issues identified in these trials were fixed, the Congress had lost the elections and the BJP was in power.

The Modi government inherited a structure for DBTs in 2014 that had already gone through the testing phase, with several schemes and the back-end tech stack in place to build on with Aadhaar. As an officer who worked closely on this in the IT Ministry told me, 'Basically, the tech stack is what Nandan Nilekani built at UIDAI. That is the software of this. Aadhaar is what was needed to make it run. Without Aadhaar it wouldn't have worked, but without the tech stack Aadhaar would have been just another ID card like many others and useless.'[11]

The journalist Pravin Kumar, resident editor of the *Times of India* in Lucknow, remembers travelling through a village, Harchandpur, near Rae Bareli, in March 2019, just before the Lok Sabha elections. While driving through, he noticed a festive atmosphere with a lot of people out on the road. He remembers stopping and asking residents if they were celebrating a festival. They told him they had just received the first instalment of Rs 2,000 in a DBT into their accounts under the PM Kisan Samman Nidhi Scheme.

Two such instalments (of a total of three annual payments) were made to 4.74 crore registered farmers in February and March 2019, just before the elections, with the Election Commission's consent. The scheme itself started on 1 December 2018.

It was formally launched by Modi on 24 February 2019 in Gorakhpur by transferring the first instalment to 1.01 crore farmers, amounting to Rs 2,021 crore.[12] Under the scheme, an amount of

Rs 6,000 per year is transferred in three four-monthly instalments of Rs 2,000 directly into the bank accounts of the farmers.

Table 4.1: PM Kisan Benefits since Inception (2018-19 to 2022-23)

Financial Year	Period	Amount (Rs)
(2018–19)	Dec–March	63,22,87,38,000
(2019–20)	April–July	1,32,71,57,40,000
	Aug–Nov	1,75,25,96,00,000
	Dec–March	1,79,25,55,86,000
(2020–21)	April–July	2,09,86,71,88,000
	Aug–Nov	2,04,69,16,98,000
	Dec–March	2,04,71,48,38,000
(2021–22)	April–July	2,23,28,04,92,000
	Aug–Nov	2,23,85,43,54,000
	Dec–March	2,23,18,58,32,000
(2022–23)	April–July	2,25,54,49,78,000
	Aug–Nov	1,79,84,92,78,000
	Dec–March	1,71,07,15,20,000
Total		**24,16,51,98,42,000**

Source: Minister of Agriculture and Farmer Welfare Narendra Singh Tomar, Government of India, Ministry of Agriculture and Farmers Welfare, Department of Agriculture and Farmers Welfare, Lok Sabha Unstarred Question No. 2124, answered on 14 March 2023.[13]

On the campaign trail in UP that year, the prime minister often referred to these payments in his speeches. As he told a Kannauj audience, 'This money is yours, it is your right, you own it. Not even Rs 2 from this money can be taken away by any government. And this won't be paid once. It will be paid thrice a year to you.'[14]

By March 2023, the number of registered beneficiary farmers under the PM Kisan scheme had risen to 11,37,00,000. Cumulatively, these beneficiaries received Rs 2.41 lakh crore, or approximately US$29.29 billion (see Table 4.1).[15]

DBT and Telangana's Rythu Bandhu: The Southern Model

Another good example is Telangana's Rythu Bandhu (Farmer's Friend) scheme. Launched in 2018, just before the assembly polls in the state, by the Bharat Rashtra Samithi (BRS)-led state government,[16] it provides farmers Rs 5,000 for each acre of land they cultivate per crop season.

Over 5.7 million farmers received their first batch of instalments in October 2018 through DBTs. This was just a month before the Telangana state elections in November 2018, so permission had to be sought from the Election Commission.[17]

Politically, this DBT scheme, until then the largest such pre-election cash transfer in India, played a major role in shoring up political support for the TRS and its return to power in 2018.[18] It is a 'revolutionary scheme', K.T. Rama Rao, Telangana's minister for IT and Industries and the party's working president, told me while on the election campaign trail in Hyderabad, soon after the scheme was initiated that year.[19] 'Nobody ever dreamt of farmers getting ₹10,000 per acre as investment support every year until Chief Minister K. Chandrasekhar Rao conceived and unveiled it,' he later emphasised.[20]

Rythu Bandhu started with nearly 50.25 lakh beneficiaries. That number increased to nearly 70.54 lakh farmers by 2023. 'Whether we use it for paying school fees or buying a few packets of seeds or for that month's consumption, Rythu Bandhu does provide us with some relief,' a Dalit farmer in Telangana's Rangareddy district told *Frontline* magazine in March 2023.[21]

Essentially, the scheme is aimed at meeting the 'initial investment needs' of farmers and 'not allowing them to fall again into the debt trap'.[22] Farmers can choose to spend the money they receive on seeds, fertilisers, labour costs or their personal consumption needs.

Rythu Bandhu started with an annual budget of Rs 12,000 crore for the 2018-19 financial year from the Government of Telangana.[23] By 2023, a total of Rs 65,559.28 crore had been spent over ten crop seasons. It became so important to the Telengana government that nearly 55 per cent of the state budget's allocation for agriculture and allied activities was used for the Rythu Bandhu scheme in 2021-22.[24]

On the flip side, one of the principal objections to the scheme has been the purported exclusion of tenant farmers, even as absentee landlords or non-cultivating landowners get benefits. There is no upper limit on landholding for a farmer to be eligible for the scheme, as *Frontline* has pointed out. In Brahmanapalle village, for instance, ground reportage by the magazine found that some farmers received less than Rs 3,000 a crop season, while others have received nearly Rs 2.5 lakh under the same scheme.

The government, in turn, claims that over 90 per cent of the beneficiaries are marginal and small farmers. As Rythu Bandhu Samithi chairman and BRS MLC Palla Rajeshwar Reddy said, 'The discontent among farmers has reduced, the distress has reduced, and so has their expenditure on inputs.'[25]

While Rythu Bandhu was successfully implemented at the state government-level, the Modi government, at the national level, followed a similar playbook with PM Kisan and other such schemes from 2019 onwards.

More Than Just Name Changes: The DBT Shift

All governments since Independence have spent money on development. The large number of Congress-era Central schemes that were renamed under the Modi regime is a case in point. At one stage, the Congress listed almost three dozen such schemes on its website—the implication being that the Modi government had somehow stolen its ideas and was taking unfair advantage of them by rebranding them.[26] This focus on nomenclature has been one of the primary critiques of the new schemes initiated by the Central government.

Several scholars have written about the Modi government's pivot to welfare and redistributive policies with these schemes. Their diagnoses have ranged from the rise of a new kind of welfare populism to the emergence of a strategy of personally linking the prime minister with these schemes as a benefactor of the poor, thus practising what has been called the politics of 'vishwas' (belief).[27]

Yamini Aiyar, president and chief executive at the Centre for Policy Research, has argued that 'more than the policies themselves, what distinguished Modi's approach to welfare was the presentation and handling of them in ways that enhanced the Modi personae. Policies that the government said had priority had the initials PM (for 'Prime Minster') added as a prefix before their names, suggesting the idea of a connection between Modi himself and the beneficiaries.'[28]

This by itself is hardly new in India. Schemes have been named after leaders of the ruling political party for decades. Among the thirty-two schemes that the Congress accused the Modi government of renaming/repackaging, three were previously named after Rajiv Gandhi, two after Indira Gandhi, and one after Nehru. The BJP chose to name three after one of its earliest leaders, Deen Dayal Upadhyaya, one after former prime minister Atal Behari Vajpayee and nine carried the generic prefix 'Pradhan Mantri'.

In UP, as chief minister between 2012 and 2017, Akhilesh Yadav provided 15 lakh free laptops to college students as part of a government scheme, each carrying photos of him and his father Mulayam Singh Yadav.[29] His government also bought 1.8 crore school bags for children with his photo and the party symbol printed on them. Ironically, many of these school bags with the Samajwadi Party (SP) symbol were later distributed by the Yogi government.[30]

Dravidian Welfarism, DMK and Enhancing the Tamil Nadu Model

Similarly, south of the Vindhyas, Tamil Nadu—which once distributed free TV sets to the poor under Karunanidhi's Dravida Munnetra Kazhagam (DMK) regime, and mixers, grinders and fans under Jayalalithaa's All India Dravida Munnetra Kazhagam (AIADMK) government—has long had a legacy of welfare schemes branded with the personality of individual chief ministers.

What DBT added was a layer of efficiency to such templates of welfare spending. In March 2023, for instance, Tamil Nadu's DMK-led government announced financial assistance of Rs 1,000 per month to women heads of eligible households under its Magalir Urimai Thogai scheme. Linking it to a significant moment in the evolution of the Dravidian movement, the then state Finance minister Palanivel Thiaga Rajan highlighted that the scheme (with a budget of Rs 7,000 crore) would be launched by Chief Minister M.K. Stalin on 15 September, the birth anniversary of late chief minister C.N. Annadurai.

The launch of the scheme, he pointed out, coincided with another important landmark. 'It is also noteworthy that the scheme is being launched in the centenary year of Muthamizharignar Kalaignar [the late former chief minister M. Karunanidhi],' he said.[31] He declared that it would be one of the biggest cash transfer schemes implemented by any state government in India's history.[32]

The DMK scheme was similar in design to a major DBT scheme for women at the state level in West Bengal, launched by Mamata Bannerjee's Trinamool Congress government in 2021. Under the Lakshmir Bhandar scheme, all women between twenty-five and sixty years of age who were not employed by the state or not drawing a pension, would get Rs 500 per month. For Scheduled Caste/Scheduled Tribe (SC/ST) women, the amount was Rs 1,000 a month.[33]

The proliferation of such schemes by 2023 was indicative of how the DBT mechanism had begun to transform the welfare architecture of India across states and across political ideologies.

DBTs and Yogi's UP Triumph

Yogi Adityanath's return to power in 2023 for a second term as chief minister of UP was directly linked to recreating the BJP as a 'party of the poor' by focusing on DBTs and schemes like housing and toilets for the poor, which directly translated into votes.

This formula of Hindutva plus development with DBT reset the old rules of Indian politics.

There were several firsts in the 2023 re-election of Yogi Adityanath, the saffron-clad mahant of the Gorakhnath Peeth, as the chief minister of India's most politically significant state. He was the first sitting chief minister of UP to be returned to power since Independence. In the days of Congress dominance, the party won successive state elections, but always with a different chief minister. The last time an incumbent party returned to power in UP was almost four decades ago. Also, the BJP actually increased its vote share from 2017, despite five years of incumbency. Its vote share was the highest ever for any party in UP since 1957.

Recreating itself as a 'party of the poor' through DBT programmes was crucial to the BJP's victory. When Adityanath took charge as chief minister in 2017, he made effective execution of all Union schemes his top priority. Modi called this a 'double-engine ki sarkar' in his campaign publicity. But what did it mean in practice?

The DBT numbers from UP are telling. It reported the highest number of total DBT fund transfers of all states in 2018-19. Partly, this was by virtue of it being India's most populous state. Even so, it was ahead by a wide margin on DBT in a state-by-state comparison of the highest-spending states (see Figure 4.1). By 2019, the DBT Mission ranked UP as No. 2 in India in its state-wise ranking on DBT.[34]

Toilets, Housing, DBT and Women

In the state of UP alone, 17.1 million household toilets were constructed between 2014-15 and 2019-20, taking the overall tally to 23.8 million in UP and 164.18 million nationally (see Figure 4.2).[35] Importantly, these toilets were not built by the government. Beneficiaries received Rs 12,000 in their bank account and had to

Figure 4.1: UP Highest in DBT Fund Transfers among All States

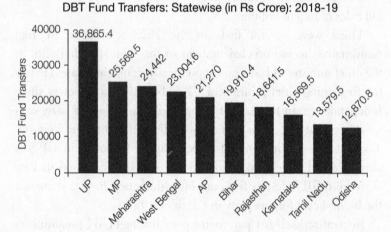

DBT Fund Transfers: Statewise (in Rs Crore): 2018-19

Source: Based on schemes for which state-wise data has been reported. As reported by DBT Mission, Government of India, 'State-Wise DBT Fund Transfer', https://dbtbharat.gov.in/page/frontcontentview/?id=NjU=.

get it constructed themselves. They received Rs 10,000 in the first tranche, and the amount that remained after the construction was verified and geo-tagged.

Revealingly, Modi began referring to these toilets as 'Izzat Ghar' or 'House of Respect' after seeing this title-plate on some toilets built in Varanasi in 2017. In a country where a lack of toilets is one of the most obvious yet underrated of gender divides, this terminology specifically targeted women.

During this period, there was a growth in housing and DBT, which also began to take centre stage in political communications. The prime minister often says in his election speeches that 'Modi's

campaign is being done by the poor brother and sister who, under
Pradhan Mantri Awas Yojana got a pakka ghar [permanent house],
got its keys and went there to stay.'[36]

**Figure 4.2: Construction of Household Toilets in UP Grew at the
Same Pace as Construction Nationwide: Swachh Bharat**

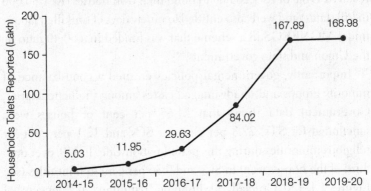

Household Toilets Constructed in Uttar Pradesh (Lakh)

Source: Swachh Bharat Mission Gramin Dashboard, Ministry of Jal Shakti,
Governmentt of India, https://sbm.gov.in/sbmdashboard/IHHL.aspx.

The PMAY-G scheme was formally launched on 20 November 2016. By April 2023, 28.5 million houses had been sanctioned under this scheme for the poor.[37] Over 22.1 million of these had already been constructed.[38] Over 3.4 million (2.6 million built) were in UP.[39] Just as with household toilets, they were not constructed by the State but funded by it.

Beneficiaries (those who lived in kaccha/dilapidated houses) received DBT of Rs 1,20,000 to build their own houses (Rs 1,30,000 in hill states) and were also entitled to ninety days of unskilled labour under MGNREGS in a scheme that was funded in a 60:40 ratio by the Union and state governments.[40]

Importantly, governmental policies ensured a good balance of minority groups and disadvantaged castes among the beneficiaries. Government data shows that 21.65 per cent of houses were sanctioned for STs, 22.8 per cent for SCs and 12.1 per cent for religious minorities during this period nationwide. In UP, over one-third of the houses went to SCs and 9.36 per cent to minorities (see Figures 4.4, 4.5). Crucially, a whopping 20 million (70.2 per cent) of 28.5 million rural houses sanctioned under PMAY-G were registered in the names of women individually or as joint holders with their husband by April 2023.[41]

This was the result of a 2016 decision by the Modi government to prioritise the commissioning of houses built in the name of a woman or jointly owned by a woman with her husband. In urban areas, the registration of houses in women's names was made mandatory in 2016. This was done, Modi explained, so that women 'get security'.[42]

The impact of this is revolutionary in a country where daughters have long been denied legal inheritance. Hindu women only got the legal right to inherit parental property in the same way as male heirs and their families in 2005 through an amendment of the Hindu Succession Act of 1956. This legal right was further expanded to women whose fathers had died before 2005 by a landmark Supreme Court judgement on 11 August 2020.[43]

Figure 4.3: Housing Construction through DBT Has Grown: Keeping in Mind Caste Groups

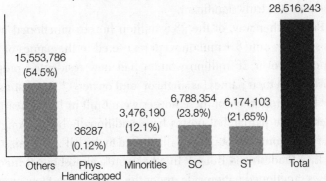

Houses for Poor Sanctioned in India, PM Awas Yojana-Grameen
(Cumulative, April 2016–April 2023)

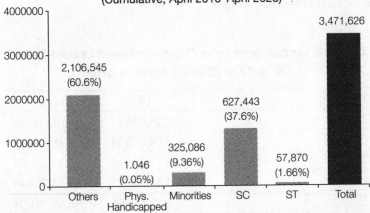

Houses for Poor Sanctioned in UP, PM Awas Yojana-Grameen
(Cumulative, April 2016–April 2023)

Source: Data from PM Awas Yojana–Gramin, Awassoft Dashboard, 'C2- Category-Wise Houses Sanctioned and Completed', 18 April 2023, https://rhreporting.nic.in/netiay/SocialProgressReport/Categorywisehouses completedreport.aspx.

In a milieu in which women faced so many barriers to equality, the fact that as many as 5.9 million rural houses that had been built under PMAY-G were registered in the names of women and another 9.2 million were registered jointly in the names of wives and husbands was truly significant.

Put another way, of the 28.5 million houses sanctioned under this scheme, only 8.4 million were registered in the names of men alone, and over 20 million women had new residential property registered in their names (as single or joint owners).[44] Interestingly, a very large proportion of these houses were built in Hindi heartland states, where patriarchal norms have traditionally been strong and where the women's vote eventually shifted to the BJP: UP, Rajasthan, Madhya Pradesh and Bihar.[45] In other words, almost one-third of all houses sanctioned nationwide under this scheme went to women in the politically important Hindi heartland states.

The decision to privilege poor women in the registration of welfare housing on an unprecedented scale embodied new possibilities and a major shift for rural women.

Table 4.2: Central Government Funds Released Under PMAY-G (2016-17 to 2022-23, in Rs, in lakhs)

Year	UP	India
2016-17	2,23,980.45	16,05,800.40
2017-18	4,94,896.43	29,88,986.14
2018-19	2,77,585.81	29,33,105.62
2019-20	1,14,564.41	27,30,584.48
2020-21	4,83,089.66	36,85,793.28
2021-22	3,72,700.20	26,23,724.44
2022-23	3,22,754.93	33,24,492.27
Total Funds Released by Centre	**17,94,675.46**	**1,98,92,486.63**

Source: Minister of Rural Development Giriraj Singh, Answer to Lok Sabha Starred Question No. 198, 14 March 2023.[46]

The Political X-Factor with 'Labharthees': How DBT Changed Local Power Equations

What is the big deal with DBT? Do such schemes make a difference and do people actually vote based on their success or failure?

The data suggests that DBTs have had a transformative power, heralding a change in local power equations. They created a new class of labharthees who could be politically harnessed.

As a senior official in the UP Chief Minister's Office (CMO) told me in Lucknow's Lok Bhawan, 'Direct transfers played a big part. If someone gets even Rs 50 in a direct transfer in his bank, then he remembers it, as opposed to the thousands of crores you spend on the public. That no one cares about or remembers at the time of elections. This creation of personal labharthees was crucial and we worked very hard to politically mobilise this with labharthee sammelans [beneficiary meetings].'[47]

A Lucknow journalist argued, 'You can make roads paved with silver and gold but nothing will happen [in terms of votes]. It is about what you get personally. That is what matters and this is why cash transfers changed the game.'

A senior functionary recounted a telling conversation with a roadside cobbler, who plied his trade opposite a doctor's clinic in Lucknow, just before the 2019 elections. When asked who would win, his response was unequivocal: 'Modi.' Why, asked the questioner, who was also carrying out a survey of Dalit voters in several constituencies. The cobbler himself was a 'haathi-waala' (Bahujan Samaj Party (BSP) supporter; the haathi, or elephant, is the party's poll symbol). So, why did he think Modi would win?

'Yes, I will vote for haathi,' he said, 'but in my village, one person has got a house [money to build one] from the government.'

Did he get a house himself?

'No,' said the cobbler. 'But I will get it. I have ummeed [hope].'

The cobbler was a diehard BSP supporter, but he had seen people in his village benefiting, and thought that he too could benefit at same stage. The possibility made him more receptive to the party itself.[48]

Of course, if spending money on welfare alone was enough to win back power, then few democratic governments anywhere would lose power. DBT as a policy tool is not some secret weapon. Liberal economists have been aggressively recommending it for years, and state governments cutting across party lines, like the BRS in Telangana or the Congress's Kamal Nath-led government in Madhya Pradesh (2018–20), have all deployed them.[49] In the case of the BJP, the massive ramp-up of DBT schemes meant that by 2023, such schemes had become a crucial lever of the party's political ascendance, apart from its emphasis on Hindu nationalism.

The Great Indian Vaccine Trick: Aadhaar, CoWIN and Public Health

The Aadhaar-enabled tech back-end for Digital India drove the digital backbone of India's great COVID vaccination effort on a scale that was unimaginable when the pandemic broke out. Indeed, at the height of the second wave of the pandemic, as the images of the dead floating in the Ganga flooded our screens, few thought that India could pull off the kind of massive vaccination campaign that was needed.

Bestselling author Chetan Bhagat seemed to epitomise the scepticism around the prospect of mass vaccination in India when he tweeted in May 2021 about what he felt was most likely to happen:

1. Rich countries would vaccinate their people first.
2. Their leftovers would finally make their way to us.
3. We'll vaccinate, and then chest thump how great we are.[50]

What happened in practice was that by October 2021, India crossed the milestone of 100 crore (1 billion) vaccination doses.[51] It took nine months after the launch of a nationwide COVID vaccination programme to reach this milestone. By July 2022, the number had crossed 200 crore (2 billion).[52] By mid-2022, India's vaccination drive was well ahead of every other country except China.

By way of comparison, Bloomberg counted Indian vaccine doses at 2.17 billion in October 2022, the EU at 912.12 million, USA at 612.8 million, Brazil at 479.1 million, Indonesia at 437 million, Japan at 321.7 million and China at 3.45 billion.

Much of India's vaccine ramp-up was driven by Aadhaar, digital certificates and CoWIN, India's open-source platform. As Bill Gates said: 'In addition to producing new life-saving tools, India also excels at delivering them—its public health system has delivered more than 2.2 billion doses of COVID vaccines. They created an open-source platform called CoWIN, which allowed people to schedule billions of vaccine appointments and delivered digital certifications for those who were vaccinated. This platform is now being expanded to support India's universal immunization program. Prime Minister Modi believes that CoWIN is a model for the world, and I agree.'[53]

What does this really mean?

In August 2022, the Norwegian diplomat and former head of the UN Environment Program Erik Solheim tweeted a video clip of India's External Affairs Minister S. Jaishankar recounting a tale of what happened when he and his son, who lived in the US, went to a restaurant together soon after the US opened up travel restrictions in 2021.

As Jaishankar recalled:

There, they wanted to see our Covid vaccination certificate. So, I showed them my phone while my son produced a folded paper from his wallet and said that it was his certificate. I looked at the folded paper and asked myself, okay, this is where they are … The whole idea of the CoWin platform was that each one of you, like me, have all the details of the vaccination with you in your phone … You must understand that this is not the case with much of the world.[54]

Jaishankar's video, which went viral in 2021, reflected the relatively under-appreciated nature of the tech back-end that drove India's vaccine scale-up.[55]

While much of the online debate on CoWIN focused on issues like each downloadable certificate bearing a picture of Prime Minister Narendra Modi—and the pros and cons of using the imagery—the political debate may have missed the wood for the trees. The fact is that this mobile and Aadhaar-enabled tech platform enabled India to roll out vaccines faster than anywhere else in the world.

The Congress party's spokesperson Pawan Khera once attacked Modi for a tardy COVID response, saying that 'if you had sent some drones over Mother Ganga at the time of COVID then you would have found out all that information that the world already had'.[56] In reality, while the government did get overwhelmed during the second wave, platforms like CoWIN allowed it to systematically ramp up vaccinations on a scale that was unprecedented anywhere in the world.

This is why, when India crossed the 2 billion vaccination mark, the BJP's Arvind Gupta wryly commented, 'As we cross #200CroreVaccinations, I guess @chetan_bhagat should tweet on learning's the west can take, from India's vaccination drive.'[57]

In fact, it would not be unreasonable to argue that vaccinations and DBTs—both delivered and monitored through the Aadhaar-enabled tech back-end—allowed the Modi government to tide over the worst of the COVID crisis. For example, Rs 36,659 crore was directly transferred into the bank accounts of 16.01 crore beneficiaries during the 2019 lockdown.[58] In parallel, between March 2020 and December 2022, the Pradhan Mantri Garib Kalyan Anna Yojana (PMGKAY) provided 5 kilograms of food grains per month to about 81.35 crore people, free of cost, over and above their National Food Security Act (NFSA) entitlement of 5 kg per person per month at Rs 2–3/kilogram.[59] This meant a spending of 3.45 lakh crore in six phases.[60] Reuters estimated it cost the government nearly US$47 billion.[61] The scheme was phased out in early 2023.

DBTs like these may explain why the Modi government did not pay a political price for the worst deprivations of the pandemic.

By mid-2023, DBT had begun emerging as a theme in the Modi government's political advertising.

A good example is the March 2023 'Mujhe Chalte Jaana Hai' campaign video released by the BJP. Showcasing the party's messaging on Modi's political journey, the four-and-a-half minute video highlights the 'Maut ke Saudagar' (Merchants of Death) and 'chaiwala' jibes he received from the Congress as Gujarat chief minister when he first made his bid for prime ministership. From his US visa being rejected by the Obama administration to being called 'hundred-head Ravan', the first 50 seconds of the video documents the political sloganeering that marked his ascent to power, before he won the 2014 election. Strikingly, the entire focus for the remaining four minutes of the campaign video is on Modi's DBT gambit. From Swachh Bharat Mission and Pradhan Mantri Ujjwala Yojana to Pradhan Mantri Jan Dhan Yojana, Pradhan Mantri Awas Yojana, PM Kisan Samman Nidhi and Ayushman Bharat, the video takes voters through the full gamut of the Modi regime's DBT schemes.

The most intriguing portion is where it shows Modi facing the COVID crisis. The animation films shows him staring into an abyss, with the coronavirus gurgling below and a broken bridge. It depicts him as rejecting the Western option of Pfizer and other vaccines, choosing the Indian vaccine and walking a tightrope across the abyss, finally reaching the 2 billion vaccine mark.[62]

The video illustrates how crucial DBT had become to the BJP's political imagery and its messaging of itself as a party of the poor. Ironically, for a party so focused on the cultural underpinnings of Hindu nationalism, it was this new welfarism through DBT that became central to its new political moorings.

5

THE HINGES
HOW UPI CHANGED INDIA AND WHY IT MATTERS

In early 2022, I undertook a 2,000-kilometre journey across some of the most backward areas of rural Uttar Pradesh. I was tracking the election campaign that brought Yogi Adityanath back to his second term in power. Astonishingly, I did not have to use cash even once.

My phone, to my pleasant surprise, worked for all money transactions, throughout the two-week-long road trip. Everywhere. Across this vast expanse of rural India, stretching from the Islamic seminary of Deoband in western UP to Sonia Gandhi's Congress stronghold of Rae Bareli, across the heart of Awadh and the seat of power in Lucknow to Pratapgarh, the Hindu holy city of Varanasi and onwards to Bundelkhand and Gorakhpur, home to the Gorakhnath peeth of the Nath tradition in Poorvanchal, the state's eastern corner.

Our team of travelling journalists only bought food from dhabas or roadside vendors. We did not stay in any fancy hotels. Yet, even roadside fruit-sellers, in regions inhabited by some of India's poorest citizens, dealt comfortably in transactions with UPI, the free back-end system that India had created for enabling seamless mobile phone money transactions between individuals, banks and merchants. In the rare case where they didn't have an app on their phone, they knew someone else who did. And the payment was done.

I had travelled exactly the same route five years earlier, in 2017, during the previous state assembly elections. Then, I had needed cash all the time. Credit cards only worked in big towns and ATM machines were few and far between. So, this time, I had come well prepared, with wads of cash drawn in advance from ATMs in Delhi. I came back without needing to spend any of it. Not only were plastic cards redundant, so was my cash. This was because the UPI-enabled system powering India is very different from the older system of ATM cards or credit cards or even e-wallets that the rest of the fintech world is more familiar with.

India recorded its highest ever UPI transactions in a month in May 2023: 9.41 billion real-time transactions conducted through people's mobile phones, with a total value of Rs 14.89 lakh crore. Data from the NPCI, which administers UPI, shows that its payment systems recorded a 58 per cent year-on-year growth in transactions in terms of volume and 43 per cent growth in value.[1]

To put this in perspective, India accounted for almost half of the world's real-time digital payments by 2023. Its share was more than the next top four countries put together—Brazil, China, Thailand and South Korea.[2]

Today, 'it's inconceivable to see a pani puri vendor, barber or cigarette seller without a QR code', concluded *Business Today* magazine in mid-2022. 'At last count, 30 million-plus merchants are using QR codes ... Mind you, there are only 6 million point-of-sale (POS) machines for swiping credit and debit cards, despite decades of presence.'[3] As one CEO told the magazine, 'UPI is now a juggernaut in its own right. It's a train that has left the station.'[4]

India's fintech revolution—there is no other word for it—is different in several ways from the way change played out in the rest of the world:

- Size and scale: Its scale is unmatched even in the developed world.
- Rural India: The growth is being powered fundamentally by rural India.

- Global adoption: The rise of digital payment systems in India now has direct implications for the rest of the world and the future of fintech. This is especially true after the Ukraine war, when US-based finance companies and the European Union weaponised control of global financial systems like Society for Worldwide Interbank Financial Telecommunications (SWIFT) by removing Russian banks from the global financial artery. As many as forty-three countries are now actively engaging with India to explore the idea of adopting UPI as an alternative mechanism for financial transactions. In early 2023, UPI was connected with Singapore's PayNow system, and then with the United Arab Emirates through Mashreq Bank's NEOPAY system. Nepal and Bhutan have been using UPI since 2022.[5]
- Common public good: Unlike elsewhere in the world, UPI is a common public good. It was initially created by a push from the State, with the Reserve Bank of India taking the initiative with a consortium of public and private banks to create the digital payments systems. It is administered as a non-profit entity, and 99 per cent of UPI transactions remain available free of cost to citizens and companies to do their business.[6] Elsewhere, the digital highways through which money transactions happen are controlled by individual private payers—or, in authoritarian regimes like China, by the State. In India, it was the State that created the digital highway and continues to run it and make it available to everyone else.
- The Making of a New State–Citizen Relationship with DBT: The fintech revolution and the coming together of cheap mobile phones, cheap data and unique IDs allowed India to bring into the banking system more people in a shorter time than any other country in the world. It allowed for a fundamental shift in the nature of the relationship between the State and the Indian poor—with DBTs on a scale that is

unprecedented in global terms and with deep implications for politics, social welfare and debates on financial inclusion.

- Scale-up to Small Businesses: This tech back-end is now being scaled up with a new government-backed e-commerce platform, Open Network for Digital Commerce (ONDC), to enable smaller businesses to sell online. Established as a non-profit company in December 2021, ONDC uses an open protocols methodology based on open-source specifications. It is different from how platforms like Amazon, which have end-to-end control over the entire transaction process, work.
- Politically planned: India's fintech revolution, powered by UPI, did not happen by accident. It was the outcome of a concerted political strategy that has changed the hinges of the Indian economy in terms of the cash flows that are its lifeblood.

The success of this Indian experiment with fintech—a 'public good gone viral'[7]—is being closely watched around the world.

'The Sound of Money': UPI and India's Fintech Revolution

The Origin Moment: BHIM App and its Political Framing

It is not a coincidence that India named its State-run BHIM (Bharat Interface for Money) app, for easy digital financial transactions using UPI, after the Constitution-maker and visionary for Dalit rights, Dr Bhimrao Ambedkar.

Few may remember today that Ambedkar, besides being an eminent lawyer, was also an economist. His first MA dissertation at Columbia University in 1915 focused on 'Ancient Indian Commerce'.[8] His second MA thesis at the London School of Economics in 1921 was entitled 'The Problem of the Rupee: Its Origin and its Solution'.[9] As India's inaugural law minister, he helped establish the First Finance Commission, which delineates funding between the Central government and the states, in 1951.

His economic ideas, presented to the Hilton Young Commission in 1925, contributed to the creation of the Reserve Bank of India.

It is to Ambedkar's deep economic influence[10] that Modi alluded when he launched the BHIM app for financial transactions on 31 December 2016. Many had wrongly assumed that the app—one among many in India that use UPI—was named after the ancient warrior-prince of the Mahabharat, Bheema.

At the launch of the app, Modi explained the thinking behind its naming:

> India's currency system, the imagination of its Central Bank and the financial system of its federal structure all had the clear darshan of one great man. The topmost contribution was of a great man whose name was Dr Bhimrao Ambedkar ... This is why we are naming the app after him ... In the coming days, all our commerce, like it used to happen with cash and coins, the day is not far when all our trade will happen over the BHIM app. In that sense, the name of Babasaheb Ambedkar is going to be centrestage in our entire economy through the BHIM app ...
>
> In the days ahead ... when people will go to Google Guru and ask what is this BHIM? In the beginning, they will see the Bheema of the Mahabharat in search results. If they dig deeper they will find that India's land gave birth to a great man like Bharat Ratna Bhimrao Ambedkar ...
>
> This technology is the greatest power. It has the power to empower the poor ... It is a myth that it is the treasure of the educated rich. It is actually the treasure of the poor. It is going to give power to the poor, to small businessmen, to farmers living in far flung villages, to tribals spending their lives in forests and this is why this great man's name has been connected to it because he gave his entire life for Dalits, the oppressed and tribals."[11]

In other words, from the get-go, Modi's fintech gambit was not aimed at rarefied boardrooms but at the 'illiterate'. Addressing those who in the past were called 'angutha-chhaap', Modi declared that UPI was meant to turn 'your thumb into your bank'. [12]

The intent and ambition were clear from the beginning, but not everybody was convinced. Modi launched UPI in 2016, the year he also announced demonetisation, his decision to derecognise existing Rs 500 and Rs 1,000 notes.[13] The app was launched just a month later.[14] With much of India lining up outside ATM machines and the economy seemingly in a flux, few expected Modi's ideas on fintech and digitising Indian finance to work.

The Congress's former finance minister P. Chidambaram's combative speech in Parliament in February 2017 typified the critique and early scepticism. Ridiculing the idea of digital payments, he questioned how it could ever work in India's villages. He also raised concerns about privacy. Citing the example of a woman at a village fair, he scoffed, 'Go to a village fair. Buy potatoes and tomatoes and pay Rs 7.50 paisa by credit card. What will the poor lady do? Does she have a POS machine there? Is it connected to an electricity source? Is WiFi there? Is the internet working there? ... What kind of false picture you are presenting?'[15]

He went on to say, 'A young lady wants to buy lingerie. Why should there be a record? A young couple wants to take a secret holiday. Why should that be recorded? I want to give money to my daughter-in-law for her expenses without the knowledge of my son. Why should there be a record? An adult wants to buy adult diapers. Why should there be a record of that?'[16]

This debate, however, was settled conclusively by the unprecedented success of UPI.

UPI Bigger Than ATMs and Credit Cards: 'By the People, of the People and for the People'

Digital money transfer systems like UPI change the way people relate to money. They also threaten the way banks, and their systems which control the networks that drive society, have traditionally functioned. For centuries, banking has been about personal interface. The smartest bankers know this. Which is why they sometimes think of digital connectivity, which connects people directly and could make traditional banking irrelevant, in terms of 'dumb pipes'. 'How can we avoid becoming dumb pipes?' the banker Piyush Gupta, CEO of DBS, South East Asia's largest bank, once asked at a conference on money in Singapore.[17] It was a question that, in many ways, articulated the fear traditional banking has of the brave, new digital world.

At its root is the emotional truth that, for most people, money is just 'the means to an end—buying a house, paying school fees and so on'. In a digitally connected world, once people can use their phones to transact money directly with each other, banks 'risk becoming invisible. Just like "dumb pipes" designed and managed by others'.[18] In that sense, bankers are right to fear these 'dumb pipes', for they have upended the system of money in India with UPI as the vehicle.

It is useful to think of UPI as the connecting pipes or—if you will—the highways that run through the economy. Entry to these highways needs an identification system and payment layers, both of which are controlled by the government. However, it is open to everyone.

This is very different from the rest of the world. 'Outside India payments tend to be handled by private firms such as Visa, Mastercard, American Express, or in China, Ant Financial and Tencent.' As *The Economist* explains, '… these [entities] own the pipes through which funds flow, and can charge heavily for their use. Their close relationships with users create high barriers to entry, putting new entrants at a disadvantage. By contrast, UPI is forbidden to charge merchant fees.'[19]

Developed and managed by NPCI, a non-profit company, UPI began operating in 2016. It was an initiative of the RBI, the Indian Banks' Association (IBA) and ten shareholding banks (later expanded to fifty-six), both private and public, with the 'intention to provide infrastructure to the entire Banking system in India for physical as well as electronic payment and settlement systems'.[20] It was designed to make sending money from phone to phone as easy as sending an SMS. And, simultaneously, be connected to the banking system.

UPI works through the 'creation of virtual accounts' which allow it to identify customers 'through various methods—from Aadhar numbers and QR codes, to the conventional sort code and account number'. Unlike, say Fedwire, the main US payments system at the time of writing, it is 'frictionless and operates around the clock'.[21] In early 2023, the United States Federal Reserve announced that it would be launching FedNow, a new instant payments solution.[22] Under this system, payments would be settled in real time, available 24/7, and for only $0.045 per transaction.[23] It will be interesting to observe how this works in practice.

A key feature of the Indian system is that, unlike many other such systems which depend on e-wallets alone, with UPI, customers can transfer money through their phones to each other. Or to merchants. Both, from their wallets or directly from their bank accounts

The Indian system is also unique because it is built as a public good tied to a national goal. It is meant to provide the enabling digital rails on which the financial system can work. It also 'enables competition', noted *The Economist*. For the 'banking system still holds all the funds. However, layered on top are a number of lightly regulated private companies, with which customers interact directly'. This means that payment apps like PhonePe (47.8 per cent of the market), Google Pay (33.6 per cent), Paytm (13.2 per cent), Amazon Pay (0.9 per cent) and others (4.5 per cent)[24] have access to account information. But they 'do not control money or network'.[25]

In practice, this means that India has a 24/7/365 system which allows citizens to send and receive money instantly using a Virtual Payments Address (VPA) set by themselves. It works person-to-person (P2P) and person-to-business (P2B), can be used over smartphone and feature phones, at merchant locations to pay utility bills, and with QR codes.

The payments system is also interoperable.[26] This means that if I buy a cup of tea costing Rs 10 from a roadside vendor and only have a Google Pay app on my phone while she only has Paytm, I can still transfer money to the vendor directly from my bank account within a second. All I need is her phone number. 'UPI is interoperable because it is designed to allow individuals to manage money residing in several accounts from a single bank or payments service app on their phone. Not only does this increase competition between banks by enabling people to switch funds cheaply, it allows fintech or big-tech interfaces—be they overlay or standalone—to work through their infrastructure.[27]

UPI succeeded beyond the dreams of its makers. It created a 'payments revolution'.[28] More Indians signed up to UPI in eighteen months than signed up for credit cards in eighteen years.[29] UPI payments grew so fast that by mid-2022, they accounted for *twice* as much as credit card and cash withdrawals combined (see Figure 5.1). So much so that, in the financial year 2022, UPI accounted for a whopping 60 per cent of retail digital payments in India.[30]

Taken together, UPI payments in value of transactions went up from Rs 17 billion in January 2017 to Rs 14.89 trillion in May 2023. In other words, they increased by 877X in this period (see Figures 5.1 and 5.2). In terms of number of transactions, UPI across apps hit a total of 9.41 billion transactions in May 2023, with high year-on-year growth rates.[31]

The initiative became such a success that hardly a week would go by when Modi, or one of his cabinet colleagues, had not showcased it in public meetings. For instance, when the data website *India in Pixels* tweeted a musical multimedia graphic to create the 'sound of money'—through a process called sonification—which depicted the revolutionary change in UPI transactions between October 2016 and mid-2022, the prime minister gleefully tweeted a message on top of the story: 'I've spoken about UPI and Digital Payments quite often but I really liked how you've used the sound of money transacted through data sonification to effectively convey the point. Very

Table 5.1: UPI's Adoption with Banks Grew at a Fast Pace
(2016–23)

Date	Banks	Volume (in Million)	Value (Crore)
April 2016	21	0	0
Aug 2016	21	0.9	3.09
Aug 2017	55	16.8	4156.62
Aug 2018	114	312.02	54,212.26
Aug 2019	141	918.35	1,54,504.89
Aug 2020	168	1,618.83	2,98,307.61
Aug 2021	249	3,555.55	6,39,116.95
Aug 2022	346	6,579.63	10,72,792.68
May 2023	447	9,415.19	14,89,145.50

Source: UPI Product Statistics, NPCI, https://www.npci.org.in/what-we-do/upi/product-statistics.

Figure 5.1: UPI Twice as Much as Card Payments and Cash
Withdrawals Combined (INR billion, in value of transactions)

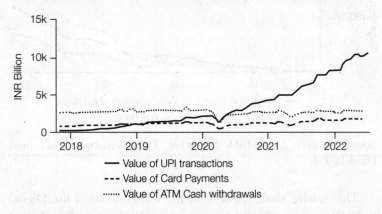

Source: Analysis by Rishabh Srivastava, Data Narratives. Data from National Payments Corporation of India, Reserve Bank of India (monthly statistics).

interesting, impressive and obviously informative.'[32] The response to
Modi's message was huge, even by his social media standards. Over
6,500 RTs and over 35,000 likes.

When my colleague, the data scientist Rishabh Srivastava, and
I checked out the district-wise data across India between 2018 and
2023, we found growth rates in rural and semi-rural India to be
much higher than in urban areas.

For example, UPI payments on PhonePe since 2018 have grown
significantly faster in rural areas like Sangli (9367.5 per cent) in
Maharashtra and Rae Bareli (6071.8 per cent) in Uttar Pradesh than
in India's Silicon Valley of Bengaluru (5237.4 per cent) or in Noida
(3141.2 per cent), home to a film city, national news channels and
a large industrial zone.

**Figure 5.2: UPI Growing Faster in Rural Areas Like Sangli and
Rae Bareli Than in Urban Areas Like Bengaluru and Noida
(YoY percentage change, March 2018–March 2022)**

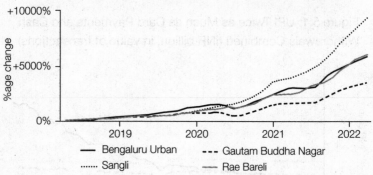

Source: Analysis by Rishabh Srivastava, Data Narratives. Data from
PhonePe Pulse.[33]

This is why Modi, speaking at the inauguration of the Digital
India Week in Gandhinagar in July 2022, directly rebutted
Chidambaram's initial critique on digitisation, made five years earlier
in the Rajya Sabha. 'Once there was a discussion in Parliament,' he

said. 'You can see it and listen to it. In that, the country's former finance minister gave a speech. "People don't have mobile phones." "How will people go digital." I don't know what all he said. If you listen to it, you will be surprised. This is what happens to people who are too educated.'

As the audience applauded, Modi continued:

Fintech, UPI, meaning Unified Payments Interface. Today the whole world is getting attracted to it. Including the World Bank, everyone has praised it as the best of the best platforms …

I say this fintech effort is, in real terms, by the people, of the people and for the people.

This technology is India's own, meaning, by the people. Indians made it a part of their lives, meaning, of the people. It made the lives of so many Indians easier in their day-to-day affairs with it, meaning, for the people. This year, in the month of May, India, you will feel proud, friends, India recorded more than 130,000 transactions per minute. Every second, an average of 2, 200 transactions were completed. Per second. This means by the time I say the words 'Unified Payments Interface', in that much time about 7,000 transactions would have been completed …

Friends, you will feel proud. Some used to call India uneducated, or this or that, etc. etc. The power of this country is such, the power of my countrymen is such that in front of developed nations of the world, when my country counts as a developing nation, in such a country 40 per cent of the world's digital transactions happen in India.

Even in that, BHIM-UPI has today emerged as a powerful medium of simplified digital transactions. And the biggest thing. Today in a mall, those who sell big brands, the technology they have access for transactions, the same technology is being used today by roadside vendors on the footpath in front of that same mall. He may be earning Rs 700–800, but these hard-working labourers have access to the same technology as the rich have in the biggest of malls.[34]

UPI's revolutionary growth mirrors the democratising intent of the original idea. This is why fintech CEOs had begun talking of it as a serious 'home-grown alternative to SWIFT' that powers most international money and security transfers, by mid-2022.[35]

In global terms, the scale of this shift has been unprecedented. India accounted for 40 per cent of total real-time payments[36] worldwide by 2021. For context, India was transacting over 2.6 times more real-time payments than China, which stood at second place (see Figure 5.3). 'An increasing adoption of unified payments interface (UPI) and QR code-based merchant payments in India, coupled with a boost to cashless payments across businesses and consumers due to the COVID-19 pandemic' led to a boost, concluded a major financial daily.[37]

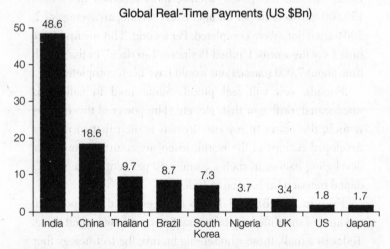

Figure 5.3: India Accounts for 40% of Global Real Time Digital Payments

Source: ACI Worldwide with GlobalData & Centre for Economics and Business Research, Prime Time for Real-Time Global Payments Report 2022, April 2022.[38]

Numbers like these led Rajeev Chandrasekhar, India's minister of state for Skills Development, Entrepreneurship, Electronics and

Information Technology, to declare that 'India is today leading the world in digital payments in particular and has become the pre-eminent country in use of technology to improve citizen's lives and governance. The India stack and other various government solutions are now the envy of the world's nations.'[39]

When I queried an official who had worked closely on the government's tech initiatives to make sense of these numbers, he responded with an analogy from physics. 'In some ways, our growth in UPI has been like it went through a wormhole,' he said. 'There is a concept of wormhole that came from Albert Einstein … If you see Christopher Nolan's film *Interstellar*, it is based on that concept. The idea of a wormhole is that if you go, for instance, from here to Surat, and by the speed of light, which is the maximum speed possible, it will take, say, for the sake of argument, eight minutes … while if you do it through a wormhole, you will cover that distance maybe in two seconds … Just like that, our digital payments suddenly zoomed from a small start to a quantum jump.'[40]

As Chandrasekhar told me in a conversation at Delhi's Electronics Bhawan, 'We were consumers of tech and not creators of tech. Today, we have digital government solutions that range from identity authentication, we have fintech, we have health online, we have tax information systems, we have analytics. We have a whole range of products and platforms that have been created to improve the technology intensity of the government. All of them have been done in an open-source manner. And see the advantages … Look at what has happened as a consequence. We have built the world's biggest fintech ecosystem in the private sector.'[41]

UPI's Global Play: Diplomacy, Fintech and India

When four of the largest US-based payment companies—Visa, Mastercard, American Express and PayPal—announced bans on transactions in Russia after it invaded Ukraine, the global landscape for UPI shifted significantly.[42] This unfolded in tandem with the

SWIFT ban on several Russian banks following a decision by the European Union to impose sanctions, which cut them off from a global financial artery that allows rapid transfer of money across borders.[43]

Irrespective of one's views on the Russian invasion of a sovereign country, the fact that the banking and credit cards of an entire country's fee-paying users could be turned off at the touch of a button was a reminder of who controls the global financial pathways. Although the payment networks were owned by private American entities, they could actually be switched off when American strategic interest was involved. 'After the Russia–Ukraine war, it is clear that UPI can be the solution,' a senior government official told me. 'People outside the West are worried about financial pathways and there is a pushback. We are seeing an embrace of UPI.'[44]

The Ukraine crisis helped crystallize the sense of vulnerability that many countries felt with respect to global financial systems. 'Imagine if you had a card in Russia. You did your bank agreements and paid your bills but still it will get cancelled without any warning,' said another official. 'There has been a lot of interest in UPI since the war ... Also, a lot of these countries were obviously worried about the pushback from the American companies and few wanted to take the first step. But now that they have seen the success of the Indian system, it makes it easier for them to tie up a partnership.'

This is a sentiment shared by many non-Western countries. As Liu Lange, chairman of the Bank of China, put it, the Western adoption of the financial nuclear option SWIFT to sanction Russia amid the Ukraine tensions is a wake-up call for China's financial sector. 'We must get prepared,' he said, 'tapping digital economy to ensure financial trade security.'[45]

It is not by accident that India has begun establishing an international ecosystem that can 'mitigate the risks of a situation— financial or geopolitical—in which traditional payment channels get disrupted'.[46] This is why India's NPCI between 2021 and 2023 entered into partnerships with banks and payment companies to enable Indian digital payment modes in several countries, including France, Singapore, UAE, Oman, Saudi Arabia, UK, Nepal and Bhutan (see Table 5.2).

NPCI set up NPCI International Payments Limited (NIPL) in 2020 to roll out India's domestic card scheme (RuPay) within the country and UPI (mobile payments) in global markets. 'Why should one reinvent the wheel? We have done it successfully in India and we want to share it with the world,' Ritesh Shukla, CEO, NIPL, told a reporter.[47]

In July 2022, Bhutan became the first nation in India's immediate neighbourhood to start using the BHIM app for mobile payments and adopt UPI standards for its QR deployment.[48] Nepal too made RuPay cards operational in 2022.[49] In the Middle East, UPI went live in April 2022 with the UAE's Mashreq Bank. This meant that Indian travellers and tourists in the UAE could now make payments through BHIM-UPI across 10,000 shops and merchant stores via NEOPAY, the payment subsidiary of Mashreq Bank.[50] The next step for India is to target remittances.

In Europe, NIPL signed up the UK's payments solutions provider PayXpert in August 2022 to make the UPI-based QR code solution available in the UK on all PayXpert's Android POS devices for in-store payments.[51] This followed a similar agreement with France in June 2022, when NPCI signed an agreement with Lyra International for UPI and RuPay cards.[52]

In February 2023, Singapore and India operationalised the link-up of UPI with Singapore's PayNow to enable a low-cost, secure and real-time option for cross-border remittances.[53] Overall, 'in some of these countries, the partnership is only for UPI, whereas in others, RuPay cards will also work at POS terminals,' reported *The Economic Times*, when it reviewed India's global push. The UPI partnerships, its reporters found, were aimed at 'enabling overseas payments through home-grown technologies, bypassing the American payment companies' like Visa, Mastercard and Amex.[54]

Table 5.2 UPI's Global Expansion

Country/Region	Partner	Date
Bhutan	Monetary Authority of Bhutan	July 2021
Singapore	Monetary Authority of Singapore, PayNow	July 2021, operationalised in February 2023
Malaysia	Merchantrade Asia and Liquid Group	Sep 2021
South East Asia and East Asia	Liquid Group	Sep 2021
United Kingdom	Terrapay, PayXpert	Feb/Aug 2022
Nepal	Gateway Payments Services, Manam Infotech	Feb 2022
United Arab Emirates	Lulu, Financial, Mashreq Bank and Network International	April 2022
France	Lyra, Worldline	June 2022
Europe (Netherlands, Belgium, Luxembourg, Switzerland)	Worldline	Oct 2022
Oman	Central Bank of Oman	Oct 2022
Saudi Arabia	TBC	TBC
Bahrain	TBC	TBC

Source: Adapted from ET Prime Research, Anand J., Sandhya Sharma, 'Why India is Taking UPI Global', Economic Times, 23 October, 2022, fieldwork.

UPI's success has provided India with a useful tool of global strategy. 'It should be seen as a hard power push by India, not a soft one. We want our payments standards to be accepted by the world,' said one diplomat who was fronting the drive. 'It is a long-term project and India needs to build the cross-border pipeline. We have pitched it to a lot of countries.'[55]

This is a long-term play that has only just begun. Its success will depend on multiple factors. Yet, it is clear that it is directly linked to India's efforts to maintain strategic autonomy and eventually even look to the rupee as a currency for international trade.[56] UPI has already started featuring in ministerial dialogues—such as one between India and France in 2022[57]—and in annual reports of the Ministry of External Affairs.[58]

Singapore's Minister for Foreign Affairs Vivian Balakrishnan, for instance, has argued that 'India has certain strengths—FinTech, digital finance, digital inclusion, and what they have done with digital identity and payment systems, is a clear opportunity for us.'

'In Singapore, of course, we have all those systems,' he told reporters after meeting India's External Affairs Minister S. Jaishankar in Cambodia. 'But for the rest of Southeast Asia, to explore how we can interconnect our payment systems, our financial systems, in order to facilitate payments and expand opportunities for small businesses across the subcontinent and across into Southeast Asia.'[59] This thinking converges nicely with India's UPI push.

The UPI–PayNow linkage in Singapore, as the RBI noted, also 'closely aligns with the G20's financial inclusion priorities of driving faster, cheaper and more transparent cross-border payments'.[60]

DigiMelas: UPI's Political Push

We were standing in a queue at an amusement park in Noida when the cashier asked a group of young men standing directly in front: would they pay in cash or by card? They were all Hindi-speaking teenagers from nearby villages. Not the kind you would expect to possess bank cards. Suddenly one of them piped up with a smile, 'Modiji has said no, go digital. So, we will pay by UPI.' They broke into loud guffaws and good-natured backslapping. But I noticed they all took out their phones and paid for their tickets digitally. When I asked the young men about the Modi comment, they responded with slightly self-conscious but proud smiles. Not all of them were BJP supporters, I realised later in conversation. Some of them voted for the Samajwadi Party, BJP's great rival in UP. But the conversation was a useful reminder of how intertwined UPI's success is with politics.

The quantum growth of UPI may seem a fait accompli now. But no one could have predicted it when the system was launched in 2016. As Chandrasekhar explained when asked about the early challenges, 'It is not easy from an execution point of view. It is not easy because of the vested interests that will fight it. It is not easy because of the political people who will oppose it. It is not easy because all of those so-called gyanis [learned ones] in Delhi—who are the status quoists—who don't like change and will say, "No, no, no ... What if, what if, what if."'[61]

The big push came politically. On 25 December 2016, the Central government, the ministry and Niti Aayog started two schemes which provided incentives for shop vendors to adopt digital payments: the Lucky Grahak Yojana and DigiDhan Vyapar Yojana. Within the first three months, by March 2017, 14 lakh people and 77,000 merchants had been disbursed a total of Rs 226.45 lakh (Rs 1,76,95,40,000 to consumers and Rs 49,50,00,000 to merchants) under the two incentive schemes. Early adopters were given cash awards. Fifteen thousand daily winners qualified for the total prize money of Rs 1.5 crore every day. In addition, 14,000 weekly winners qualified for prize money of over Rs. 8.3 crore every week.[62] The idea was that 'if you did digital payments, you will get so many incentives. It was a cashback scheme'.[63]

Figure 5.4: The Digital Payments Push: Union Government
Advertisements Promoting 'Lucky' Shoppers and 'Digi"
Businesses, 2016

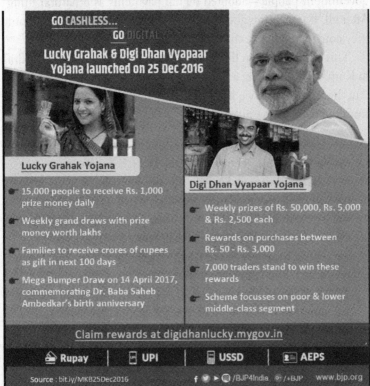

Source: https://twitter.com/PIB_India/status/812268594402709506?s=20;
https://twitter.com/BJP4India/status/813604101950873600?s=20.

Significantly, Modi fronted this push, lending his political weight to the drive. Large full-page advertisements were printed in newspapers. As a senior government official recalls, 'The ministry took big advertisements out—in six steps, how digital payments are done, whether you have mobile with data, feature phone or smart phone, Aadhaar-enabled payment or not. They showed how with six steps you can close a transaction.'[64]

Saurabh Kumar, additional commissioner of GST, who served as personal secretary to Ravi Shankar Prasad, IT minister at the time, points out that the key factor was 'how fast people—and I mean government people—adopted digital payments as a natural thing'. After all, if few in the government believed in the idea, how would they convince others to make the shift?

This may have been the reason why, in February 2016, according to Kumar, Modi sprang a surprise on the team. 'The PM told us one day,' he recalls, 'that we have to do one hundred digital fairs in one hundred days.' As he put it:

Everybody who was involved said this is impossible. They said this can't be done. Three times (teen teen baar) meetings were held. Then Principal Secretary of the PM said this won't be possible. And they used to go and request to the PM that Sir, this won't be possible. The PM said—there is a noting in the file on the last meeting—that if it won't be possible, you don't do it, but it has to be done: one hundred meetings in one hundred days. Somebody else will do it. And finally, everyone got mobilised. Till the District Magistrate-level, everybody was mobilised. All the ministries were mobilised. A team was made that used to go and teach in rural areas how digital payments are to be made.

Today we may not think of this as a big deal or we are not aware, but this educated the entire system one hundred per cent. What may have otherwise taken five years, ten years, educating village after village, in hundred days it was done.

These fairs were christened DigiDhan Melas. 'There was a full team of fifty to hundred people here who were themselves first trained. They understood all the questions. Then they used to go to each mela and used to explain how this will happen. We held a hundred melas in a hundred days and all over the country. DMs [district magistrates], SDMs [sub-district magistrates] were all involved.'[65]

The first aim was to educate the government itself. Once that was done, the programme managers would move on to meeting ordinary citizens. 'They used to call shopkeepers. Because if the shopkeeper doesn't enable the receiving of digital payments, however much someone wants to use it, how will they? So, shopkeepers were called. They [officers] used to explain to them how to use [UPI].'

The officers coordinating these melas started seeing initial results. But their efforts were unfolding in the period immediately after demonetisation and doubts remained. 'If you look at the graph, I remember that time there used to be an entry—this is above the trending line but it is an effect of demonetisation,' says Kumar. 'We used to wonder how long will this progress last.'[66]

Initially, as part of the government initiative to popularise digital payments, DigiDhan Melas were organised in 100 cities over a period of 100 days in twenty-six states and seven Union Territories. In this initial push, over '5,000 financial institutions ... reached fifteen lakh citizens through the melas and at least 16,000 government and private institutions were declared cashless'.

The melas were held in places as diverse as Gangtok and Imphal in the northeast, Haridwar in the north and Nellore in the south. One result was that the BHIM app was downloaded 18 million times in the first three months after its launch. By August 2022, this number had increased to 50 million.

As an official told me, 'For the first six months, people used to keep doing commentary—when will it fall? When will it fall? It never fell. The commentary stopped. That was how it was in mainstream media. The fact is that we have virtually been hitting an all-time high every month. Every month has seen UPI hitting all-time highs since.'[67]

By March 2022, Bloomberg's Andy Mukherjee could declare that 'fintech is everywhere in India'. So much so that its 'banks need a counter-attack'. As he put it, 'Visit a mid-sized store in an Indian city, and you'd wonder if it exists to make any money. It might just as well be there to process transactions for half-a-dozen payment apps: PhonePe, Paytm, Google Pay, BharatPe, Amazon Pay and MobiKwik. Add up the merchants who have downloaded the digital services and the figure quickly reaches 80 million. A third of India's 60 million-plus small businesses are using an average of four different platforms.'[68]

Ahead of Web 3.0: UPI as a 'Special Public Good'

The rise of UPI has huge implications for the future of fintech itself. Chatting over coffee at Googleplex, Google's headquarters in California, on a hot, sunny day in May 2019, Caesar Sengupta, the man who then headed the company's initiative to get the Next Billion Users worldwide and Digital Payments, told me that he had been 'absolutely stunned' by how UPI had expanded. India was ahead in digital payments, he stressed, compared to any other country in the world. His team had set up Google Pay in India, working with the UPI system, and he quickly discovered that 'what you can do with UPI in India, you still can't do here in California or in Washington'.

'When we started, UPI was a very new system and had only existed for about eight or nine months,' he said. They had been pleasantly taken aback, he said, by how fast it expanded. By this time, about two-thirds of Google Pay payments were already being done in small towns and rural India, outside the eight big metros. It had clocked forty-five million users at the time, about US$80 billion (annualised) were passing through its systems and about 5–6 per cent of India's GDP was estimated to be moving through UPI. 'That's stunning and it's happened in eighteen months … We are actually very humbled and surprised by the adoption,' said Sengupta.[69]

So, how is UPI different? At a big-picture level, how does it compare to other systems in the West? And why does it matter globally?

This was the question I put to the Silicon Valley tech entrepreneur, technologist and academic Vivek Wadhwa in late 2022. We were seated in his central Delhi hotel room, and Wadhwa, who has held senior positions at Harvard Law School, Carnegie Mellon, Stanford and Duke universities, had just managed to get his own UPI account up and running.

'Look, Apple Pay was launched about seven years ago,' he said. 'And to date, very few places accept it. Hardly anyone uses digital currencies. Globally, when they talk about the digital economy, they think about crypto, about Bitcoin. And Bitcoin is a Ponzi scheme. It's completely useless as a currency. It died as a currency long, long ago. So, they have no concept of a digital economy in America.'

UPI changed things for India, he says. 'Before, when you came here, India was a backward country. Now, it is far more advanced. Even the beggars now have barcodes, in places. They want you to scan to give them money. Yeah, everyone does. People don't prefer money anymore, post-COVID. They think money is filthy, which is exactly what it is. So, everything has changed over here. And the United States has been left behind. Not just United States, it's the whole of the world which has been left behind … UPI works lightning fast.'[70]

Earlier in the year, Wadhwa had co-authored an important and provocative piece arguing that while the rest of the world was still thinking about Web 3.0, India had raced ahead with UPI. 'For more than a decade, Silicon Valley's moguls have been promoting Bitcoin and blockchain-based cryptocurrencies, claiming these will transform global commerce. Instead, Bitcoin long ago died as a digital currency, becoming nothing more than an empty speculative asset,' Wadhwa and his co-authors, the technologists Ismail Amla

and Alex Salkever, argued. 'Meanwhile, as those same hypesters now
promote a mystical Internet world called Web3, India is racing ahead
and implementing what the crypto crowd had promised—with
its Unified Payments Services (UPI) ... delivering a real revolution
that flies under the radar of the tech gurus in England's Shoreditch
and America's Silicon Valley.'[71]

They identified seven major factors that make UPI stand out as a
global model. I list them here, with one addition of my own:

- Proof of concept: UPI has been shown to work well for a very
  large population.
- Open protocols: '... upon which other technologies can
  be built, creating a much larger and more useful network
  than its competitors for financial payments ... exactly what
  blockchain was supposed to do—cutting out intermediaries
  and inducing greater competition.'
- Democratising e-commerce: Opens up new possibilities
  to 'democratize e-commerce and reign in the technology
  companies that are building monopolies'.
- Neutral marketplace, low cost: The Reserve Bank of India
  has placed explicit limits on market share in UPI payments
  to be implemented initially by January 2023 (deadline
  extended at the time of writing to 31 December 2024). The
  implementation time frames for these are being negotiated
  again,[72] but the principle is in place.[73]
- DBTs to the poor: 'Prior to UPI, corruption, bureaucracy,
  and a chaotic banking system made it nearly impossible for
  the government to reliably send money to the poor', but UPI
  offered 'affordable access to real-time payments to hundreds
  of millions of people'.
- Security: UPI was designed to require strong two-factor
  authentication, 'making it more impervious to fraud than the
  older systems in richer countries'.[74]

- Free platform: UPI transactions were free of cost to 99.9 per cent of consumers till mid-2022. While there is a strong debate now[75] whether UPI payments should be charged or not, it will 'eventually cost only a tiny fraction of what merchants and consumers pay to move money on private payment systems such as those run by Mastercard and Visa'.
- Digital public good and interoperability (my addition to this list): The reason why UPI payments are free is because the State saw UPI as 'digital public good', as India's Ministry of Finance declared in August 2022.[76]

When India took over the G20 presidency for 2022, this was one of the priorities it identified for the global high table.[77] As Harsh Shringla, India's chief G20 coordinator and then foreign secretary, noted at the Raisina Dialogue in Delhi, 'Our startup sector, a world beating digital public goods industrial policy, focused on technological innovation and growth show that we are capable of creating tech models that balance the need for global integration and priorities at a national level.'[78]

Importantly, already existing digital payment systems like credit and debit cards require the payer and buyer to make a transaction on the same system and have limited interoperability. So, an American Express or Mastercard will only work on an American Express or Mastercard-enabled point-of-sale machine. Not so with UPI, which is interoperable across platforms, allows users to pay money through a financial highway that is free of cost and works no matter which service provider is paying whom. All are interconnected.

When I asked Wadhwa about his diagnosis in Delhi, he was even more gung-ho. 'I wrote a very optimistic article,' he said. But 'things are moving faster than I thought. This gives India a huge advantage.'

Arguments like these are a major reason why Google recommended the UPI and its lessons to the US Treasury for path-adoption. When the US Treasury decided to support a new system called FedNow, Google officially wrote to the Board of Governors of the Federal Reserve, recommending its India experience. 'UPI was thoughtfully planned and critical aspects of its design led to its success,' wrote Mark Isakowitz, vice president for Government and Regulatory Affairs, Google USA and Canada. He listed several advantages of UPI:

- It was an interbank transfer system
- It is a real-time system.
- It is an 'open' system, which means technology companies can build applications that help users directly manage transfers into and out of their bank accounts.

'The approach in India,' he concluded in November 2019, 'attained amazing results for banks, consumers, other players within the payments ecosystem and India's central bank ... After just three years, the annual run rate of transactions flowing through UPI is about 10 percent of India's GDP ... Remarkably, the use of debit, credit and pre-paid cards also nearly doubled during the same period ... This system successfully encouraged close collaboration between technology and financial services providers, and created winning opportunities across the ecosystem.'

Among its recommendations Google emphasised a 'Standardized API [application programming interface] integration' like in India.

In India, the provision of such a standardized API has enabled technology companies to quickly integrate and work with over 140 banks that utilize the UPI system. In contrast, in economies where such a standardized API is not available, or one in which technology companies are not provided access, more complex and sometimes incompatible API standards have required custom work for integration between each pair of technology and financial services companies. Absent a standardized API, smaller financial services companies with more limited resources face greater challenges in joining the new digital ecosystem.[79]

With barely concealed delight, Saurabh Kumar, the former IT Ministry bureaucrat who was involved with much of the early UPI work, says that when he first heard about the Google recommendation, he thought it was a fake WhatsApp forward. 'When I saw that letter [from Google] my first reaction was it could be a fake letter,' he said. 'I thought maybe someone made it for propaganda. Then I verified it with Google. They said no, it is a correct letter. It is an authentic letter.'[80]

Beyond Amazon: India's E-Commerce Play

The success of UPI led India to bet on an ambitious new system of e-commerce. The Open Network for Digital Commerce (ONDC) started off with grocery and food stores in Bengaluru in September 2022.[81] Its eventual aim is to bring almost 60 million mom-and-pop stores or neighbourhood shops onto a common platform to revolutionise the country's supply chain ecosystem. The Bengaluru launch followed a pilot project in forty-five cities.[82]

Like UPI, ONDC was built by using open controls for e-commerce. ONDC owes it origins to several strands of thinking, like Atmanirbhar Bharat and the 'Anti-Big Tech' sentiment. Its genesis lay in the concerns expressed by small businesses about deep discounting and predatory pricing on e-commerce platforms.[83]

The Government of India, under the Ministry of Commerce, set up a committee in mid-2021 to create an alternative. This included, among others, Nandan Nilekani of Infosys, who had set up India Stack and UIDAI, Arvind Gupta from the BJP and NPCI, R.S. Sharma who set up the CoWin app, and veterans from retail/restaurant associations. Following the same broad principles as UPI, it created a system with interoperable APIs.[84] Unlike platforms like Amazon or Flipkart, which control the entire e-commerce transaction from start to end, ONDC was meant to 'unbundle' or break down this complex system into separate micro-services that could be done by any entity.[85]

As Commerce Minster Piyush Goyal said, 'India has about 6 crore small stores that employ about 10 crore people. Large ecomm platforms use big data and algorithms to promote products of their choice. As consumer affairs minister it is my job to ensure that people get full information of the products available and their choice is not limited to what the big companies want to promote.'

How would this work? As he put it, 'The small mom-and-pop, localised stores can create small, localised networks … Supposing someone wants to order a bottle of water, they will know through this network that a neighbourhood shop has a particular one they want and can quickly deliver. While we can't wish away the emergence of e-comm (giants), this will give small stores visibility.'[86]

While it is too early to predict the future of ONDC at the time of writing, the ambition is clear. By end-2022, India had begun moves to directly link UPI to credit cards,[87] to enable loans through it. An analysis of UPI payments showed that P2P payments accounted for nearly 80 per cent of total transaction value, whereas person-to-merchant (P2M) payments made up the balance. This was 'partly thanks to the roaring cash-back culture that encouraged people to download payment apps'.[88] Many observers expected it to power the next phase of growth through increasing person-to-merchant transactions.[89]

As the Nobel Prize–winning economist A. Michael Spence argued, India has become a 'powerhouse' in the digital realm. 'It has a thriving digital ecosystem—and in India, instead of digital systems replacing existing retail systems, entrepreneurs and companies are building solutions to integrate existing and sometimes very small retail businesses into digitally enabled supply chains, making them more effective.[90]

Did UPI Kill the Toffee?

My generation of Indians grew up with the idea of most neighbourhood stores giving you a toffee instead of change. Entire candy businesses were built on this idea of change and cheap toffees—typically costing Rs 1 or less. So powerful has UPI's rise been that in mid-2022 it was blamed for the demise of the toffee.

Abhishek Patil, the founder of GrowthX, argued in a viral LinkedIn post that candy brands Mondelez, Mars, Nestle, Perfetti Van Melle, Parle and ITC used to own the 'chhutta' (change). When 'UPI penetration went through the roof', it 'killed the candy business'. As he put it:

> Before UPI, shopkeepers would shamelessly trade toffees for loose cash, a transaction that wasn't happening the other way round. These small amounts over days wound up becoming large sums of money, as accepted by many buyers in studies. With UPI, all of this stopped. People paid the exact amount that was due with no scope for change, ultimately eating up the daily toffee sales. The pandemic added fuel to the fire …
>
> No chocolate (toffee) company would have ever thought of finance products as their competition …
>
> Evolve your product offering & distribution so you don't get a UPI like shock.[91]

While this claim has been challenged, the very fact that it could be made[92] showed how effectively UPI had captured the Indian imagination and the economy.

6

NUTS AND BOLTS
ASSESSING THE HARDWARE THAT POWERED THE DIGITAL SHIFT

Digital India would have meant little without the creation of hardware that was needed to make it run. The best intentions, policies, product designs and software stacks would have come to nought without connectivity. Internet connections, even with Wi-Fi, need wiring. Digital tools need the physical connections that enable them to get networked. The success of Digital India, therefore, depended in great measure on the expansion of two hard-coded requirements: infrastructure and manufacturing.

'Amateurs talk strategy, professionals talk logistics,' as military men often say, in a quote attributed to General Omar Bradley, the World War II veteran. It is easy to get carried away by the seductiveness of grand ideas. And Digital India is as grand as they come. But its realisation—and the making of India's techade—was powered by a massive increase in hardware, the nuts and bolts that drove India's digital revolution and access across the traditional digital divide.

The Hardware: Optical Fibre Cables, Towers and Rats in Village India

The numbers tell their own story. Between 2014 and 2022, India went from 251.1 million internet connections to 836.9 million (an increase of 232 per cent). Broadband connectivity went up by a whopping 1,238 per cent, from 61 million to 816.2 million connections. The numbers of mobile towers almost doubled, going up from 4,00,000 to 7,40,000.

They were interconnected with a giant spider web comprising a total of 3.55 million route kilometres of optical fibre cables (OFC), either dug underground or laid out overhead by various internet providers—mostly private ones, licensed by the State.[1] Of these, 6,00,898 kilometres of OFC were laid out to villages by the government-owned BharatNet, which was created specifically to bring rural India online.

For perspective, in 2014, only 359 kilometres of such OFCs had been laid out to villages. Only 60 gram panchayats had been connected by such wires. By 2022, as many as 1,90,364 gram panchayats had service-ready OFC connectivity (see Table 6.1).

Table 6.1: The Hardware of Digital India

Item	2014	2022	% Change
Total phone connections	93,30,10,000	1,17,02,00,000	25.42
Mobile connections	90,45,10,000	1,14,40,00,000	26.4
Internet connections	25,15,00,000	83,69,00,000	232.7
Broadband connections	6,10,00,000	81,62,00,000	1,238
Average cost per GB of data per subscriber	268.97	10.29	-96.17
Average monthly data consumption per wireless data subs	61.66 MB	16.4GB	27,235.8
Mobile Base Transceiver Stations (BTS)	800,000	2,398,000	199.75
Mobile towers	400,000	740,000	85

Item	2014	2022	% Change
Optical Fibre Cable laid (BharatNet) to villages	359 km	6,00,898 km	1,67,281
Gram panchayats connected with optical fibre cables.	60	1,90,364*	3,17,173.3

* 1,82,131 were service-ready: 1,77,665 gram panchayats with OFC and 4,466 over satellite. Source: Yearly reports by TRAI, Ministry of Communication.[2]

Soon after he first took oath as prime minister in 2014, Modi had stated that 'cities in the past were built on river banks. They are now built along highways. But in the future, they will be built based on availability of optical fibre networks and next-generation infrastructure.'[3] By 2022, much like in China earlier, the digital highways that powered India's techade had been laid out through a massive expansion of broadband connectivity.[4]

In a country that is still almost 70 per cent rural, how digital connectivity reached India's villages matters. Internet infrastructure specialists say that OFCs made up of glass fibres are about twenty times faster than traditional cables, which are mostly made of copper.[5] They are also more durable. Professors Robin Jeffrey and Assa Doron, the pre-eminent historians of telephony in India, have noted that one reason why the reach of telephones expanded so slowly in India in the first four decades after Independence was because of its vastness but also because the wires used to link up some 6,00,000 villages to telephones were made largely of copper. 'Copper was valuable ... Not surprisingly, rural phone wires sometimes disappeared.' Then there was the problem of durability and rats.

In the early 2000s, when telecom engineers began working on rural connectivity, one group in the western state of Maharashtra came across the remnants of public computers in a village, placed there as part of an information and communication technology

(ICT) project for rural computer connectivity put together by Rajiv Gandhi's regime in the late 1980s—except that the 'cables had apparently been chewed by rats'.[6] As they wryly noted, 'Maharashtrian rats were not alone in enjoying a nice cable dinner. In the US, sharp-toothed Brooklyn squirrels brought author Andrew Blum's telecom connections crashing down as he was writing his 2012 book about the physical infrastructure that makes up the internet.'[7]

This is why OFCs held so much promise. It was this cabling that enabled the creation of CSCs, which powered the rural penetration of Digital India. India had 5,23,208 active CSCs by March 2023, of which 4,15,228 were at the gram panchayat level. That is, almost 80 per cent were in rural areas.[8]

Modi often refers to this expansion in his speeches. In 2020, for instance, he declared from Delhi's Red Fort that 'if you see, prior to 2014, only five dozen panchayats had the optical fibre network. However, in the last five years, 1.5 lakh panchayats were connected with optical fibre ... We are working on the goal of taking it to every panchayat and this work is in progress in the remaining one lakh panchayats ... In the coming 1,000 days, every village in the country will be connected with optical fibre.'[9]

How did this happen? Again, the Modi government inherited a structure and plan for connecting Indian villages with broadband cables from the Manmohan Singh regime. Called the National Optical Fibre Network (NOFN) initiative, it was launched in 2011 and intended to create an 'information superhighway' for India to reach the 'unreached'. Bharat Broadband Network Ltd (BBNL) was set up by the government as a special purpose vehicle for this in 2012.

However, by 2014, only a few dozen panchayats had been connected. Because NOFN did not reach its targets in time and costs went up substantially, it was redesigned and rechristened as BharatNet in 2015, with revised targets. With an estimated total outlay of Rs 72,000 crore, its aim was 'to provide on demand, affordable broadband connectivity of 2 Mbps to 20 Mbps for all households and on demand capacity to all institutions, to realise the vision of Digital India, in partnership with States and the private sector'.[10]

'There were multiple issues with NOFN,' a senior official who served in the IT Ministry at the time told me. He explained:

> Actually, the whole design we inherited [in 2014] was not a very good design. So, we had to make a lot of changes. For example, if the equipment of BharatNet has to be kept in a village, where will it be kept? What will that house or place be in the village? That was also not very clearly identified. So, somebody kept it in the Panchayat Bhawan. But there are many places where there is no electricity in a Panchayat Bhawan. There is not even a door or a window in a Panchayat Bhawan in many places. So that whole equipment became unsafe. There were some people who kept it in a school. Somebody kept it in a temple—whatever they could find.[11]

This was not dissimilar to other experiments with State-led television in the decades before the internet. In a village in Puducherry, in 2008, I had found a government television set installed in the village temple. It was part of a government scheme for development programming. When village officials tried looking for an appropriate place to install it in the 1990s, they couldn't think of a better place than the temple courtyard, where the whole community congregated in the evenings.[12]

BharatNet, which aimed to connect all of India's 2,50,000 gram panchayats with broadband, had to overcome many inherited design issues. 'We found that little thought had gone into the fact that if you lay the infrastructure, it will get cut, it will get damaged,' an official explained. 'Somebody has to repair it, somebody has to upgrade it, and so on. This plan was also missing in the design and technology that we inherited.' If somebody asks what is the difference between NOFN and BharatNet, then this is the crucial difference, he added. 'There are still some challenges. Not to say that there aren't. The country is so diverse. Somewhere the states are helpful. Somewhere the panchayats are helpful. Some places are there where they are not very cooperative. There are those challenges. The terrain is difficult or diverse. It is not so easy to dig trenches in hilly areas, marshy areas. There are terrains in the country where the river shifts its course and the whole village gets submerged. It has its own challenges.'[13]

By 2023, government data showed that BharatNet had connected over 76 per cent of its targeted area. In Almora, for example, broadband came to Basoli Takula village in 2021. Neeraj Singh, the CSC operator in the village, says that 'before 2021, I used to offer services through BSNL. Now the digital services are through fibre optic cable.' His village in Almora is one of the 1,93,420 villages in India that had been connected with OFCs by June 2023.[14]

While a lot of progress has been made, significant challenges remain. Critics have raised questions on the quality of connectivity, speed of implementation and rising costs. Some of these challenges informed the cabinet decision in 2022 to merge BBNL, the public body that ran BharatNet, with BSNL, the state-owned telecom provider.[15] How BharatNet managers tackle these challenges going forward will determine if they can meet the government's declared target of 2025[16] to connect all gram panchayats with OFCs.

India's Great Submarine Cable Bet

Cables don't just matter domestically. They are also needed for external connectivity. Just as pipelines transport oil, submarine cables transport data. By 2023, about 500 submarine cables were estimated to be carrying about 97 per cent of global internet traffic. The remaining 3 per cent were serviced by satellites.[17] These undersea cables drive the global digital economy.

Just as Britain, at the height of its empire, controlled two-thirds of the world's subsea cables in the age of the telegraph, control of submarine cables and the location of data centres have become central to the running of the modern digital economy. As an Observer Research Foundation (ORF) special brief by the US-based Atlantic

Council's Kaush Arah has pointed out, Amazon, Google, Microsoft and Facebook have invested in over forty cables since 2010. Their collective ownership in miles is estimated at 63,605 for Google, 57,709 for Facebook, 18,987 for Amazon and 4,104 for Microsoft.[18]

India's techade gambit and its growing digital push also means that Indian companies are now making substantial investments in submarine cables. By Arah's count, India, by 2021, had about seventeen submarine cables terminating at fourteen distinct cable landing stations in five cities: Mumbai, Chennai, Kochi, Thoothukudi and Thiruvananthapuram. The existing cable landing stations are owned by Tata Communications (five), Bharti Airtel (three), Reliance Jio (two), Global Cloud eXchange (formerly Reliance Globalcom) (two) and others, including Sify, BSNL and Vodafone.

By early 2023, several new cable links with India at their centre were in various stages of construction. These included the Reliance Jio initiative to make the world's largest submarine cable system centred in India. This initiative consisted of:

- India–Asia Xpress (IAX), stretching from Singapore to Mumbai with branches in Matara (Sri Lanka), Satun (Thailand) and Morib (Malaysia).
- India–Europe Xpress (IEX), connecting Mumbai to Europe with landings in the Middle East and Africa (Oman, Djibouti, Saudi Arabia and Egypt), as well as France, Italy, Greece and the US East Coast.[19]

Stretching across 16,000 kilometres, both IAX and IEX are major strategic projects. They got approval from the expert appraisal committee of India's Ministry of Environment in late 2022.[20] Reliance Industries has stated that this is the 'first time in the history of fibre optic submarine telecommunications' that India has been placed at the centre of the international network map.[21]

The ORF study pointed to other India-linked projects in 2023:

- MIST, connecting Mumbai and Kochi to Myanmar, Thailand, Malaysia and Singapore, is an 8,100-kilometre cable with a capacity of 218 Tbps. It is funded by a Japanese joint venture and built by NEC.
- Blue-Raman, stretching from Italy to India, is funded by a Google-led consortium that includes Telecom Italia Sparkle and Omantel.
- SEA-ME-WE 6 upgrades the link from Singapore to Marseille, traversing 19,200 kilometres. It is funded by a traditional consortium of telecommunications companies from Singapore, Malaysia, Indonesia, Bangladesh, Pakistan, Maldives, Sri Lanka, Saudi Arabia, Egypt, Djibouti and France. Bharti Airtel has joined the consortium and is funding about 20 per cent of the costs.[22]

Taken together, this sampling of submarine cable projects indicates how critical India has become to the strategic subterranean arteries that control the digital world.

India's Electronics Surge: Powered by Smartphones

A big growth in electronics manufacturing is the critical second strand in India's digital story. The increase in the export of electronic goods, driven by a surge in shipments of mobile phones, is a telling measure of how India has shifted registers on this count.

In 2022-23, India's estimated electronics exports shot up by over 50 per cent to US$23.6 billion, overtaking readymade garments, a traditional mainstay of Indian export. This made electronics the sixth biggest Indian export, just a little lower on the list than the US$25.4 billion drugs and pharmaceuticals sector, which has grown steadily because of the large-scale export of generic medicines (see Table 6.2). It was a big shift, though India remains a net importer in this category.[23]

Table 6.2: Smartphone Surge: Electronics Exports
Ahead of Garments

Top Exports (US$Billion)	FY22	FY23	%Change
Engineering goods	112.2	107	-4.6
Petroleum goods	67.5	94.5	40
Gems and jewellery	39.1	38	-2.8
Chemicals	29.4	30.3	3.1
Drugs and pharma	24.6	25.4	3.3
Electronics	15.7	23.6	50.3
Readymade garments	16	16.2	1.3
Top Imports (US$Billion)	FY22	FY23	%Change
Petroleum	161.8	209.6	29.5
Electronics	73.7	77.3	4.9
Coal, coke, etc.	31.7	49.7	56.8
Machinery	39.9	45.4	13.8
Gold	46.2	35	-24.2
Chemicals	30.3	33.4	10.2
Stones*	31	30.7	-1.0

*Pearls, precious/semi-precious. Source: Commerce Department data, collated by *The Times of India.*[24]

The growth was driven primarily by an increase in mobile phone exports, which hit US$11 billion in 2002-23.[25] Apple and Samsung accounted for the largest share. Apple's iPhone exports from India grew nearly four times to cross US$5 billion in FY 2022-23, while the figure for Samsung was between US$3.5 and US$4 billion.[26]

These numbers meant that, by 2023, India had turned into the second largest phone manufacturer in the world. 'Ten years ago, 98 per cent of the mobile phones that we were using in India were imported,' says Ashwini Vaishnaw, India's minister for Communications, Electronics and IT. 'Today, 98 per cent are made in India.'[27] From just two mobile phone factories in 2014, India now has over 200 such units. Samsung opened the world's largest mobile phone factory in Noida in 2018. Apple, which used to produce about 1.5 per cent of its global shipments of iPhones in India in 2020, took this up to 5–7 per cent of global shipments in 2022.[28]

The remarkable rise of phone manufacturing in India has generated a great deal of debate. It has often been attributed to the government's production-linked incentives (PLI) scheme. But there are those who ask whether India has actually become a phone manufacturing giant or simply a place where phone kits are being assembled by global companies for export. The economists Rahul Chauhan, Rohit Lamba and Raghuram Rajan, for instance, have argued that 'very little apart from assembly is done in India, though manufacturers claim they intend to do more in the future'.[29]

The nub of this debate is the 'value-addition' that is required to be done by phone manufacturers. Under the PLI scheme, the government expects eligible players to achieve a domestic value-addition of 40 per cent by 2026. Current estimates for value-addition by vendors assembling various iPhones were reported to be in the range of 12–15 per cent (compared to around 40 per cent in China).[30]

On balance, it may be said that countries looking to transform their manufacturing trajectories have to begin somewhere. The massive shift currently underway in phone manufacturing in India signifies a shift in mindset. It indicates how India, by 2023, had emerged as a major base for global phone companies as they looked to diversify their supply chains from China. And we know that both China and Vietnam focused on globalising before they localised.[31]

India seems to be drawing on these lessons as it changes gears. While we are in the early stages of this process, the direction of change is clear. The expansion of the infrastructure base that underpins Digital India is well and truly underway, with the first results now becoming visible.

7

INDIA'S TECHADE
WHAT'S NEXT ON DIGITAL FUTURES?

Few believed in India's digital revolution when it started. However, systems like Aadhaar, UPI, DBT and the CoWIN app, which laid the base for it all, have fundamentally transformed India at multiple levels. The very idea of digital public infrastructure (DPI)—created by the state and available for usage on scale—directly changing people's lives is a powerful one.

By early 2023, India had begun to significantly expand its digital footprint. There were moves to deploy a new 5G stack and embark on new tech collaborations with the United States. These shifts, along with India's advocacy of digital public goods during its G20 presidency, reflected the country's confidence not just in the power of its digital tools but also their efficacy as instruments for local and global force projection.

The creation, management and control of digital networks is just as vital to the fortunes of nations today as the making of rail networks and telecommunications was in the nineteenth and early twentieth centuries. India's championing of DPI as part of its G20 presidency in 2022-23 was predicated on the fact that it became the first country, through India Stack, to develop the three foundational nodes that are essential to creating an effective DPI ecosystem: digital identity

(Aadhaar), real-time fast payments (UPI) for money flows and data management through secure financial data sharing systems like the Account Aggregator network (launched in 2021, regulated by the Reserve Bank of India and built on the Data Empowerment Protection Architecture or DEPA).[1]

India's digital public infrastructure grew rapidly because its components were designed as 'rails'. Each rail addressed 'a specific need', as a recent IMF paper by Siddharth Tiwary, Frank Packer and Rahul Matthan pointed out.[2] These 'rails' or 'foundational DPIs' provided the 'backbone' of the country's digital infrastructure.[3] Tech innovations followed, and the building of a powerful set of new apps by government and businesses 'across several of these rails that could be scaled up to … over a billion people in 29 states [changed to 28 states after the revocation of Article 370 in 2019] and 22 languages'.[4]

This also enabled the creation in India of 'open networks' of a kind 'not seen before', observe Samir Saran and Sharad Sharma of the Observer Research Foundation. By 2023, India was developing such open networks for credit (Open Credit Enablement Network), commerce (Open Network for Digital Commerce), health (Open Health Services Network and United Health Interface, or UHI) and other domains.[5] A crucial differentiator, as the IMF says, was that 'unlike other countries where the digital infrastructure was developed largely by private companies, India put together a unique model of digital public infrastructure, publicly designed and controlled but privately implemented'.[6]

Digital India had opened up new opportunities, but also raised several new challenges. In the age of OpenAI, the metaverse and breathtakingly fast technological changes, any writing about technology runs the risk of becoming outdated even before it is printed. Yet, I would like to outline three broad strands on emerging possibilities and five major challenges at this point in time.

The 5G Stack

India began rolling out 5G services in October 2022. By early 2023, over 50 million Indian 5G customers accounted for about 5 per cent of the world's 5G consumers.[7] It was not just the speed. A big difference from previous such telecom rollouts in India was the governmental emphasis on deploying indigenous tech for 5G.

'What gives bigger happiness is the development of India's own 4G and 5G technology stack,' Ashwini Vaishnaw, IT minister, declared in early 2023. 'It was initially tested for 1 million simultaneous calls, then for 5 million, and now it has been tested for 10 million simultaneous calls. It is a phenomenal success. There are at least 9-10 countries that want to try it out … Today there are two Indian companies which are exporting to the world. In the coming three years we see India as a major telecom technology exporter.'[8]

As in the case of India Stack before it, Indian policymakers focused on catalysing indigenous tech with 5G. The government decided to restrict foreign telecom vendors from the mega 4G and 5G modernisation projects at the State-owned BSNL and MTNL. 'Forget old loyalties,' Vaishnaw told officials at these networks in mid-2022, insisting that 'only and only the technology which is "Made in India" has to be used in all network upgrades to 4G and 5G'.[9] The government-owned Centre for Development of Telematics (C-DOT), for instance, designed the Non-Standalone (NSA) 5G core.[10] C-DOT (with its core technology) and Tejas Networks (for its radio networks) were part of a consortium led by Tata Consultancy Services (software support and system integration) that won a Rs 19,000-crore BSNL contract in 2023 for enhancing its 4G network.[11]

Just as with the systems that came before it—identity authentication, payments, health—Indian policymakers were looking to export the new indigenous 5G stack built through public–private partnerships.[12] 'For decades India had been a consumer of tech and not a creator of tech,' Rajeev Chandrasekhar, minister of state for IT, told me at his office in Delhi's Electronics Bhawan. 'Computers were being made somewhere. We bought them and we used them. Telecom networks and gear were being made somewhere. We bought and deployed them … Prime Minister Modi wanted India to be in the leading pack of nations that will shape the future of the internet and the future of tech. And today we are. Today we have digital government solutions that range from identity authentication to fintech to health to tax information systems … We have a whole range of products and platforms that have been created to improve the technology intensity of government.'

Specifically on 5G, he asserted, 'For the first time, we are deploying for the 5G network, which is a state-of-the-art, latest generation wireless network, gear that is being designed in India and manufactured in India.'

It was essentially the same sentiment that animated Reliance Industries Chairman Mukesh Ambani's announcement in July 2020 of Reliance Jio's 'made-in-India' 5G technology solutions that he said were built from scratch and used '100 per cent homegrown technologies'.[13] This was envisioned as the cornerstone of the company strategy for creating a digitally connected ecosystem in India and overseas.

While the 5G shift was still in its incipient stages, the ambition was unambiguous.

Size Matters

India's digital revolution is not just about India. The country accounted for 21 per cent of the global mobile traffic in 2022, up from just 2 per cent in 2021. Only China (25 per cent) was bigger. But the fact that it is closed to outsiders underscored the importance of the Indian market for global tech players.[14]

Domestically, in real terms, the Reserve Bank of India estimated that the share of the core digital economy rose from 5.4 per cent of gross value added (GVA) in 2014 to 8.5 per cent in 2019.[15] Further, the share of the digitally dependent economy (digitally enabled sectors) was estimated to be 22.4 per cent in 2019.[16] The seismic shifts undertaken by Digital India meant that even a seasoned banker like former ICICI Bank chairman K.V. Kamath, now the chairman of the National Bank for Financing Infrastructure and Development, has argued that digital could account for as much as 25 per cent of the Indian GDP by 2029.[17]

Earlier estimates, such as in a study by the Ministry of Electronics and IT, had estimated that India's digital market size could go up to between US$200 and US$500 billion by 2025 if things continued as usual. It had the potential to zoom to US$1 trillion by 2025 if a series of policy measures were followed.[18] While projections vary— Google, Temasek and Baine and Company jointly estimated that India's digital economy would constitute 12–13 per cent of its GDP by 2030[19]—the direction of change was clear.

The New Age of 'AI'

The growth of Digital India has also provided new ballast to Indian diplomacy. The change in India–US relations is a case in point. When Modi visited the US in early 2023, technology was centre stage. As the prime minister put it during his address to the joint session of the US Congress, 'In the past few years, there have been many advances in AI—artificial intelligence. At the same time, there have been more momentous developments in another AI—America and India.' Going beyond the semantics, which got a standing ovation from US lawmakers, this evocative phrasing reflected the seismic nature of the shifts underfoot, in relation to Indian tech.

It is not an accident that the India–US joint statement released after the meeting between Prime Minister Modi and US President Joe Biden started with a section on 'Charting a Technology Partnership for the Future'. Signalling the new emphasis, the statement mentioned the words 'technology' or 'technologies' as many as forty-three times. For perspective, when Modi and Biden met for their first-ever bilateral meeting at the White House in September 2021, the joint statement released at that time mentioned 'technology' or 'technologies' only fourteen times. The 3X difference in the 'tech' word cloud over the past two years is a measure of the shift. As were the investments announced at the 'Hi-Tech Handshake' with big tech CEOs: Google with its global fintech operations centre in Gujarat's GIFT City and US$10 billion for the India Digitisation Fund, Amazon with an additional US$15 billion till 2030 (taking its total India investment to US$26 billion), Microsoft's Jugalbandi AI assistant for government services, powered by AI4Bharat, a government-backed initiative, and reasoning models from Microsoft's Azure OpenAI Service.[20]

Tech cooperation was once a small sidenote in the India–US relationship. It is now at the forefront. Ranging from quantum computing to AI to cybersecurity to outer space, this new focus on a strategic partnership in high-tech and commerce, coming as it does at a time when China-oriented global supply chains are being reconfigured, has wider implications for global tech architecture.

A case in point is the focus on semi-conductors—as evidenced by agreements with Micron Technology to invest up to US$825 million to build a new semiconductor assembly and test facility in India with support from the Indian government, Lam Research's proposal to train 60,000 Indian engineers through its Semiverse Solution virtual fabrication platform, and an announcement by Applied Materials, Inc. to invest US$400 million to establish a collaborative engineering centre in India. The wider backdrop to this is the American decision to restrict China's access to US semiconductor technology as a security measure over fears that it was becoming over-dependent for chip production on its biggest strategic foe.[21] While this is still an evolving story and a lot of work remains to be done, it indicates a turning point for India's semiconductor vision and its ambition of integrating with global manufacturing and supply chains for high-end tech.

While Digital India has become a major aspect of India's economic growth and its global soft power projection, significant challenges remain:

- The Need for New Regulation: At the domestic level, the new reality needs a new regulatory structure. The regulatory structure around Digital India, at the time of writing, still hinged on the Information Technology (IT) Act, 2000. This legislation was written before the dotcom bust and before the rise of mass e-commerce and social media platforms.

  In 2000, the Indian internet encompassed just 5.5 million people. It had risen to 850 million by 2023, making India the world's largest 'digitally connected democracy'. It had also grown from just one kind of intermediary to multiple types: social media platforms, OTT channels, e-commerce, gaming and AI—along with a proliferation of hate speech, disinformation and fake news. Though the IT Act has been amended several times since, the regulations are far behind the reality.[22]

  ⅄ Old structure: With the IT Act at its centre, the old regulatory structure included a maze of other interlinked structures, such as:
    - the Intermediary Guidelines and Digital Media Ethics Code, 2021[23]
    - Certifying Authority Rules, 2000[24]
    - Indian Computer Emergency Response Team (CERT) for digital security threats[25]
    - Reasonable Security Practices and Procedures and Sensitive Personal Data or Information (SPDI) Rules, 2011[26]

- Procedures and Safeguards for Blocking for Access of Information by Public, 2009[27]

▲ Proposed new structure: At the time of writing, the government had announced plans to replace the old regulatory architecture with a new one. This meant a series of legislations and new rules, broadly divided as below:

  - At the core of the new architecture lay the draft Digital India Act.
  - Linked to it was the Digital Personal Data Protection Act, 2022 (this followed an earlier version which was withdrawn in 2022)[28]
  - The Digital India Act Rules
  - IPC amendments for cyber crime
  - National Data Governance Policy

While it would be premature to comment on the detailing of the new architecture, which is still evolving, it is pertinent to outline some of the contentious points in the emerging discourse:

- Concerns on Security: As India goes global with its DPI, assuring foolproof security of digital systems is a key public concern. In early 2023, reports of a Telegram bot that was throwing up personal data of vaccinated people, purportedly from the CoWIN app, rang alarm bells. The government strongly denied that the CoWIN database had been 'directly breached' and indicated that the bot might have been throwing up stolen/breached data from the past.[29]

  The UIDAI has also denied previous reports of data breaches in the Aadhaar database.[30] Government policymakers like R.S. Sharma have often emphasised the foolproof nature of the OTP verification systems such platforms deploy.[31]

  Security concerns are as much about trust and perception as they are about facts. They will matter even more as India's

DPI systems go global. India, by July 2023, had put together a National Data Governance policy, a draft of which had been finalised at the time of writing,[32] which would create a common framework of data storage, access and security standards across government institutions.[33]

- Concerns about a 'Surveillance State': The Supreme Court of India ruled in 2017 that the right to privacy is a fundamental right protected under Article 21 and Part III of the Constitution.[34] While a new legislation for protecting data, the Digital Data Protection Bill, 2022, was being made ready for parliamentary discussion as this book went to press, privacy activists have raised concerns on two counts: the extent of exemptions to the Centre and its agencies for access on grounds of national security, public order, etc., and the role of the government in appointing members of proposed data protection boards that would deal with grievances on privacy.[35] As privacy activist Apar Gupta argued, the concern was about the 'expansion of state power that tilts the law against the interests of individual privacy' and 'concentration of power in the executive branch'.[36] In other words, the concerns hinged on whether there would be adequate protections against possible misuse of private data by State actors.

  Debates on these issues between the two extremes of privacy and national security are par for the course in any democracy. Striking a fine balance between the two imperatives will likely define the success of the proposed legislation.

- Sovereignty and Big Tech: Union Minister Rajeev Chandrasekhar suggested in March 2023 that 'we [India] actively think to do away with Section 79 safe harbour [in the IT Act] completely, and say that it is the responsibility of the platforms that post the content. To do whatever due diligence they have on misinformation, on toxic content, illegal content, and that government doesn't get into it'.[37] His contention, raised as part of a dialogue on the Digital India Act, went to the heart of the wider global debate on the tensions between sovereignty, Big Tech and global information flows.

The idea of safe harbour—the principle that intermediary Big Tech social platforms are not liable for information, data or content posted by third parties on their platforms— has been a central tenet of the internet as we know it. Safe harbour should not mean blanket immunities, argued the minister. Most platforms encourage user anonymity, he pointed out, while enjoying protections under Section 79. As such, would it not be prudent to move from 'blindfold immunity to conditional immunity'?

At one level, this contention opened up the larger debate around social media platforms taking accountability for the content hosted on their platforms. It also raised the question of digital sovereignty and whether platforms should uphold the laws of the land they operate in or some other standard set up elsewhere, in a different context. The platforms, of course, pushed back, saying that 'safe harbour' was fundamental to the way they operated and that changing the rules would make it impossible for them to function. As MediaNama's Nikhil Pahwa argued, 'Remove safe harbour and the internet would not be able to survive. Start Up India would not be able to survive.'[38]

Even as liberal democracies around the world are debating the nature of digital sovereignty at a time of unprecedented transnational information flows, the outcomes from the debate in India will be keenly watched.

- DPI@Global: At the global level, while India seeks to shepherd a global take-up movement on DPIs, three kinds of institutions need to be built. As Samir Saran and Sharad Sharma have argued in a recent paper, a robust global expansion would first need the setting up of 'independent DPI steward institutions'. This would need multi-party

governance, as opposed to control by a single party, in order
to build trust. A good example of this is MOSPI, at the
International Institute of Information Technology, Bangalore.
The second requirement would be the creation of global
standards through a multilateral dialogue led by India. And
finally, the development of sustainable financing models for
developing DPI for the world.[39]

Other challenges remain, notably on content regulation and
mechanisms for controlling fake news.[40] How some of these debates
unfold will define the contours of the next stage of Digital India.

India's digital transformation is, after all, a work in progress. Its
trajectory depends on the wider evolution of the Indian political
economy. By 2023, it had become clear that a solid foundation had
been laid and India had made a 'quantum leap' in digital terms.
The revolution engendered by Digital India, along with initiatives
like Make in India, Start Up India and Skill India signal a change of
direction for the world's largest democracy.

'The history of international affairs is in many ways the history
of technology,' India's External Affairs Minister S. Jaishankar told
a Bangalore audience a few years ago.[41] In that sense, on balance,
Digital India has initiated a new paradigm in India's growth journey.

NOTES

INDIA'S DIGITAL TECHADE: AN INTRODUCTION

1. See, for instance, PM Narendra Modi's assertion in July 2021, on the sixth anniversary of Digital India, the Government of India's flagship programme for creating a digital society, that 'top experts are looking at this decade as India's techade', https://twitter.com/ANI/status/1410493207213871106?s=20; also see Modi's Independence Day speech from the Red Fort on 15 August 2022. Our Bureau, 'India's Techade Bringing Digital Revolution to Grassroots Level', *The Economic Times*, 16 August 2022, p. 1.

2. Data from PIB, Ministry of Electronics and IT, 'Achievements Made Under Digital India Programme', 23 December 2022, https://pib.gov.in/PressReleaseIframePage.aspx?PRID=1885962.

3. Monthly data from 'UPI Product Statistics', https://www.npci.org.in/what-we-do/upi/product-statistics; RBI data quoted in Sangeeta Ojha, 'Online Payments in India: How UPI is Changing the Face of Digital Payments', *Mint*, 20 June 2023, https://www.livemint.com/money/personal-finance/online-payments-in-india-how-upi-is-changing-the-face-of-digital-payments-11687241104262.html.

4. Data from MyGovIndia, https://twitter.com/mygovindia/status/1667207266888740864?s=20.

5. Data from PIB, Ministry of Electronics and IT, 'Achievements Made Under Digital India Programme', 23 December 2022, https://pib.gov.in/PressReleaseIframePage.aspx?PRID=1885962.

6. *The Economist*, 'How India is Using Technology to Project Power', 4 June 2023, https://www.economist.com/asia/2023/06/04/how-india-is-using-digital-technology-to-project-power.

7. Sundar Pichai's statement in Washington, 24 June 2023, is available at https://twitter.com/PTI_News/status/1672349987953418240?s=20.

8. Ministry of External Affairs, 'India's Forthcoming G20 Presidency', 13 September 2022, https://www.mea.gov.in/press-releases.htm?dtl/35700/Indias_forthcoming_G20_Presidency.

9. Full text of Narendra Modi's speech at Bali, 16 November 2022, is available at https://pib.gov.in/PressReleseDetail.aspx?PRID=1876347.

10. Amitabh Kant's interview with Sidhartha and Surojit Gupta, 'India Will Take Up Challenges of Growth, Jobs, Climate during Its G20 Presidency', *The Times of India*, 5 December 2022, p. 17.

11. Quoted in Our Bureau, 'India to Push Digital Public Goods at G-20: Sherpa Kant', *The Economic Times*, 12 April 2023, p. 14.

12. Anand Adhikari, 'The Giant Killer', *Business Today*, 15 September 2022, https://www.businesstoday.in/interactive/longread/upi-the-made-in-india-payments-system-is-rocking-not-just-india-but-is-making-waves-globally-too-171-15-09-2022.

13. Pranav Mukul, 'Explained: How Indians Now Make Payments Using UPI in UAE', *The Indian Express*, 23 April 2022, https://indianexpress.com/article/explained/explained-indians-payments-upi-uae-7881510/.

14. https://mosip.io/about.php.

15. PMJDY data, from Ministry of Finance, PIB, 28 August 2022, https://www.pib.gov.in/PressReleasePage.aspx?PRID=1854909.

1. THE BUILD

1. PM Narendra Modi's comments in meeting with Nalin Mehta at 7 Lok Kalyan Marg, New Delhi, 8 April 2022.

2. Full text of PM Narendra Modi's speech at the inauguration of International Exchange at GIFT City, 29 July 2022, available at https://www.narendramodi.in/mobile/text-of-pm-s-address-on-the-occasion-of-inauguration-of-the-india-international-exchange-at-gift-city-gandhinagar. For more context on the GIFT City, see, for instance, Suchitra Karthikeyan, 'Explained: GIFT City: The History and Tax Incentives of India's First "Smart City", *The Hindu*, 29 August 2022, https://www.thehindu.com/business/gift-city-explained-history-tax-incentives-of-indias-first-smart-city/article65736969.ece.

3. This classification was by the Association of Democratic Reforms, which studied the wealth of candidates. See, for instance, *Business Standard*, 'Nandan Richest Candidate in 2014 Polls', 9 April 2014,

reproduced in https://adrindia.org/media/adr-in-news/nilekani-richest-candidate-2014-polls; also see PTI, 'Modi Wave Sinks Nandan Nilekani in Lok Sabha Elections', *Mint*, 16 May 2014, https://www.livemint.com/Politics/FPXAt2uVAoxRRuURs18t3J/Before-election-results-Nandan-Nilekani-concedes-defeat-in.html.

4. Anisha Nair, 'War of Words: Modi Slams Nilekani, Claims Credit of IT Development', 9 April 2014, https://www.oneindia.com/bengaluru/war-words-modi-slams-nilekani-claims-credit-it-development-lse-1427563.html?story=2.

5. Nandan Nilekani, 'Imagining Technology as a Governance Tool', in Bluekraft Digital Foundation (ed.), *Modi@20: Dreams Meet Delivery* (New Delhi: Rupa, 2022), p. 267.

6. Interview with a former government official, speaking on condition of anonymity, 6 April 2022. For more details on this, see, for instance, Mail Today Bureau, 'Montek, Chidambaram Call Truce on UID Feud as Manmohan Singh Steps In', *Business Today*, 26 January 2012, https://www.businesstoday.in/latest/policy/story/montek-singh-ahluwalia-p-chidambaram-uid-war-manmohan-singh-28642-2012-01-26; Kumar Shakti Singh, 'When NPR, Aadhaar Caused a Rift Within UPA 8 Years Ago', *The Times of India*, 27 December 2019, https://timesofindia.indiatimes.com/india/when-npr-aadhaar-caused-a-rift-within-upa-8-years-ago/articleshow/72996421.cms.

7. Interview with a former government official, speaking on condition of anonymity, 6 April 2022.

8. This point has also been noted by the journalist Shankkar Aiyar in his history of Aadhaar. See, for example, Shankkar Aiyar, 'How Aadhaar Got a Second Life Under PM Modi', *The Times of India*, 6 July 2017, https://timesofindia.indiatimes.com/india/how-aadhaar-scheme-got-a-second-life-under-pm-modi/articleshow/59464487.cms. For more details, see Shankkar Aiyar, *Aadhaar: A Biometric History of India's 12-Digit Revolution* (New Delhi: Westland, 2017). For a short summation of this, see this short video, https://www.youtube.com/watch?v=WBVRdsjsCx8.

9. Interview with a former official, with knowledge of the matter, speaking on condition of anonymity, 6 April 2022.

10. Nandan Nilekani, 'Imagining Technology as a Governance Tool', in Bluekraft Digital Foundation (ed.), *Modi@20: Dreams Meet Delivery* (New Delhi: Rupa, 2022), pp. 267–68.

11. Ibid, p. 268.

12. Vikas Dhoot and M. Rajshekhar, ET Bureau, 'Nandan Nilekani Impresses Narendra Modi and Arun Jaitley, Gets Aadhaar a Lifeline', *The Economic Times*, 24 July 2014, https://economictimes.indiatimes. com/news/economy/policy/nandan-nilekani-impresses-narendra-modi-arun-jaitley-gets-aadhaar-a-lifeline/articleshow/38940461.cms.

13. Nandan Nilekani's was responding in a Q&A session moderated by Nalin Mehta following his keynote speech, 'Rebooting the Republic', at Times Lit Fest Delhi, 26 November 2016. Full video of this session is available at https://economictimes.indiatimes.com/news/et-tv/times-litfest-delhi-nandan-nilekani-talks-about-rebooting-the-republic/videoshow/55635414.cms?from=mdr.

14. Nandan Nilekani, 'Imagining Technology as a Governance Tool', in Bluekraft Digital Foundation (ed.), *Modi@20: Dreams Meet Delivery* (New Delhi: Rupa, 2022), p. 267.

15. Quoted in Sonia Singh, 'Only PM Modi, Sonia Gandhi Questioned This About Aadhaar: Nandan Nilekani', NDTV, 4 June 2019, https://www.ndtv.com/book-excerpts/rahul-gandhi-offered-me-hrd-ministers-job-in-2009-nandan-nilekani-2047900. For more details, see Sonia Singh, *Defining India: Through Their Eyes* (New Delhi: Penguin, 2019).

16. Interview with a former official, with knowledge of the matter, speaking on condition of anonymity, 6 April 2022.

17. Vikas Dhoot and M. Rajshekhar, ET Bureau, 'Nandan Nilekani Impresses Narendra Modi and Arun Jaitley, Gets Aadhaar a Lifeline', *The Economic Times*, 24 July 2014, https://economictimes.indiatimes. com/news/economy/policy/nandan-nilekani-impresses-narendra-modi-arun-jaitley-gets-aadhaar-a-lifeline/articleshow/38940461.cms.

18. Mahendra K. Singh, 'Modi Govt to Give Legal Basis to Aadhaar', *The Times of India*, 14 July 2014, https://timesofindia.indiatimes.com/india/modi-govt-to-give-legal-backing-to-aadhaar/articleshow/38336812.cms.

19. This was the Aadhaar (Targeted Delivery of Financial and Other Subsidies, Benefits and Services) Act, 2016. See details on passage of the Act at https://prsindia.org/billtrack/the-aadhaar-targeted-delivery-of-financial-and-other-subsidies-benefits-and-services-bill-2016. For a critical view of this, see, for instance, Arvind P. Datar and Rahul Unnikrishnan, 'Aadhaar: The Money Bill Controversy', https://www.

barandbench.com/columns/aadhaar-money-bill-controversy; for the government's defence on the pros of Aadhaar vs the argument on the fundamental right of privacy, see the then finance minister Arun Jaitley's speech in Rajya Sabha while introducing the Aadhaar Bill, 16 March 2016, https://www.youtube.com/watch?v=n_xVirhYZmg.

20. Surabhi Agarwal, 'Aadhaar Gets a Second Life from Modi', *Business Standard*, 28 October 2014, https://www.business-standard.com/article/current-affairs/aadhaar-gets-a-second-life-from-modi-114102800024_1.html. For more details on how various Hindi news TV channels—ABP, India TV and Aaj Tak—covered the issue at the time, see the compilation available at https://www.youtube.com/watch?v=xRijhGlLgV4.

21. Quoted in Surabhi Agarwal, 'Aadhaar Gets a Second Life from Modi', *Business Standard*, 28 October 2014, https://www.business-standard.com/article/current-affairs/aadhaar-gets-a-second-life-from-modi-114102800024_1.html.

22. The constitution bench was led by Chief Justice of India (CJI) Dipak Misra. The majority judgment of the Supreme Court was written by Justice A.K. Sikri in concurrence with CJI Dipak Misra and Justice A.M. Khanwilkar. In his concurring decision, Justice Bhushan said the Central government had given sufficient reasons to uphold Section 7 of Aadhaar Act, which deals with grant of subsidies and welfare benefits. The dissenting judgment was by Justice D.Y. Chandrachud who argued that Aadhaar was violative of Article 110 and critiqued the decision to pass the Aadhaar Bill as a Money Bill in the Lok Sabha, where the government had an absolute majority. Overall, the apex court upheld the Aadhaar Act of 2016 but struck down some sections of the Act, including Sections 33(2), 47 and 57. It read down Section 33(1). Express Web Desk, 'Supreme Court Rules Aadhaar Not Mandatory for Bank Accounts, Mobile Numbers, School Admissions', *The Indian Express*, 26 September 2018, https://indianexpress.com/article/india/aadhaar-verdict-supreme-court-judgment-uidai-5374829/. Also see Express Web Desk, 'Aadhaar Verdict: All You Need to Know About the Supreme Court Ruling', *The Indian Express*, 26 September 2018, https://indianexpress.com/article/india/aadhaar-verdict-all-you-need-to-know-about-the-supreme-court-ruling-5374717/.

See full text of the SC judgment, Writ Petition (Civil) No. 494 of 2012 Justice K.S. Puttaswamy (Retd.) and Others vs Union of India and Others, 26 September 2018, available at https://uidai.gov.in/images/news/Judgement_26-Sep-2018.pdf.

In 2021, the Supreme Court, by a majority 4:1 verdict, also dismissed a review petition seeking a review of its 2018 judgment on Aadhaar. TNN, 'Supreme Court Rejects Aadhaar Review Plea in 4:1 Verdict', *The Times of India*, 21 January 2021, https://timesofindia.indiatimes.com/india/supreme-court-rejects-aadhaar-review-plea-in-41-verdict/articleshow/80375919.cms.

For a critical view on Aadhaar and issues of privacy, also see B.N. Srikrishna and Swapnil Kothari, 'Expanding Aadhaar to Private Entities is Risky', *The Hindustan Times*, 18 May 2023, https://www.hindustantimes.com/opinion/expanding-aadhaar-to-private-entities-is-risky-101684335170719.html.

23. Aman Sharma, 'Accessibility, Funds, Logistics: Nandan Nilekani on Modi being the "Driving Force" Behind Aadhaar', CNN-News18, 23 November 2021, https://www.news18.com/news/india/accessibility-funds-logistics-nandan-nilekani-on-modi-being-the-driving-force-behind-aadhaar-4478846.html.

2.   THE BUILD, PART 2

1.   For a break-up of the authorised registrars and their contribution to Aadhaar registrations, see UIDAI Dashboard available at https://uidai.gov.in/aadhaar_dashboard/registrar.php.

2.   Canalys, 'Indian Smartphone Shipments Up 10% to 137 Million in 2018, Unfazed by Global Decline', 7 February 2019, https://www.canalys.com/newsroom/indian-smartphone-shipments-up-10-to-137-million-in-2018-unfazed-by-global-decline. Also see PTI, 'India Beats US to Become 2nd-largest Smartphone Market in Q3: Canalys', *Business Standard*, 9 November 2018, https://www.business-standard.com/article/current-affairs/india-pips-us-to-become-2nd-largest-smartphone-market-in-q3-canalys-118110801258_1.html.

3.   'Data Usage Per Smartphone Is the Highest in India—Ericsson', *Ericsson.com*, 19 June 2019, https://www.ericsson.com/en/press-releases/2/2019/6/data-usage-per-smartphone-is-the-highest-in-india-ericsson. By 2019, India accounted for 12 per cent of the world's internet users, China 21 per cent and USA 8 per cent. See Mary

Meeker's Internet Trends 2019 Report, 11 June 2019, https://www.bondcap.com/report/itr19/#view/1.

4.   The Nokia MBIT Index 2023 reported that mobile data traffic in India increased threefold during 2018–2022, reaching over 14 exabytes per month. *Nokia Annual Mobile Broadband Index Report 2023*, https://www.nokia.com/about-us/company/worldwide-presence/india/mbit-index-2023/.

5.   See also IANS, 'One Indian Mobile User Now Consuming 19.5GB Average a Month', *Business Standard*, 16 February 2023, https://www.business-standard.com/article/technology/one-indian-mobile-user-now-consuming-19-5gb-data-on-average-a-month-123021600535_1.html; Assa Doron and Robin Jeffrey, *The Great Indian Phone Book: How the Cheap Cell Phone Changes Business, Politics and Daily Life* (London: Hurst and Company; republished in the US by Harvard University Press, 2013).

6.   TRAI, 'Highlights of Telecom Subscription Data as on 31 January 2022', Press Release no. 17/2022, 30 March 2022, https://www.trai.gov.in/sites/default/files/PR_No.17of2022_0.pdf.

7.   *Ericsson Mobility Report*, November 2022, p. 23, https://www.ericsson.com/4ae28d/assets/local/reports-papers/mobility-report/documents/2022/ericsson-mobility-report-november-2022.pdf.

8.   PIB, 'English Rendering of PM Modi's Speech at India Mobile Congress & Launch of 5G Services in India', 1 October 2022, https://www.pib.gov.in/PressReleseDetailm.aspx?PRID=1864152.

9.   Telecom Regulatory Authority of India (TRAI) in mid-2019 reported 581.51 million internet users in India. Information Note to the Press (Press Release No. 49/2019), TRAI, New Delhi, 19 July 2019, https://www.trai.gov.in/sites/default/files/PR_No.49of2019.pdf; Information Note to the Press (Press Release No. 37/2014), TRAI, 7 July 2014, https://trai.gov.in/sites/default/files/PR-TSD-May%2C%2014.pdf.

     By 21 August 2019, TRAI was reporting that wireless data subscribers had increased to 578.21 million. https://trai.gov.in/sites/default/files/PR_No.61of2019.pdf.

     The 2022 numbers are from TRAI, Press Release No. 67/2022, 18 October 2022, https://www.trai.gov.in/sites/default/files/PR_No.67of2022.pdf.

India had 910,512,091 voters in the 2019 general election. Source: Election Commission of India, https://eci.gov.in/files/file/10991-2-highlights/.

10. Google estimated average mobile data consumption per user to be about 8 GB/month in early 2019. Google, *Unlocking Digital for Bharat* (Delhi: Google, 2019). Data from Bain & Company, quoted in the report, p. 2.

11. Between 2014 and 2018, it increased by 29 times, going up to 7.69 GB per person in 2018. The 2022 data is from *Nokia Annual Mobile Broadband Index Report 2023*. Older data is from CSDS, *Social Media and Political Behaviour* (New Delhi: Lokniti-CSDS, 2019), pp. 11–22.

12. CSDS, *Social Media and Political Behaviour* (New Delhi: Lokniti-CSDS, 2019), pp. 11–22.

13. See, for example, Nalin Mehta's interview with Caesar Sengupta, Google vice president, Next Billion Users and Digital Payments, at Google HQ in May 2019, '95% of Video Consumption in India Is in Regional Languages; Hindi Internet Users Will Outnumber English by 2021', *The Times of India*, 17 May 2019, https://timesofindia. indiatimes.com/blogs/academic-interest/95-of-video-consumption-in-india-is-in-regional-languages-hindi-internet-users-will-outnumber-english-users-by-2021/; Nalin Mehta's interview with Ajit Mohan, vice president and managing director, Facebook India, 'There is Clearly a Shift from Offline to Online … People are Looking for Richer Experiences on Virtual Presence', *The Times of India*, 22 July 2020, https://timesofindia.indiatimes.com/blogs/academic-interest/there-is-clearly-a-shift-from-offline-to-online-people-are-looking-for-richer-experiences-on-virtual-presence/.

14. See, for example, Robin Jeffrey and Assa Doron, 'Mobile-izing: Democracy, Organization and India's First "Mass Mobile Phone" Elections', *The Journal of Asian Studies*, Vol. 71, No. 1, February 2012, pp. 63–80.

15. ANI, 'UIDAI Has Issued 70 Crore Aadhaar Numbers till Oct 28, 2018', *Business Standard*, https://www.business-standard.com/article/news-ani/uidai-has-issued-70-crore-aadhaar-numbers-till-oct-28-2014-114102800979_1.html.

16. Aadhaar Dashboard data, April 2022, in https://uidai.gov.in/images/Aadhaar_Brochure_July_22.pdf.

17. Aadhaar Dashboard data, 25 May 2023, https://uidai.gov.in/aadhaar_
dashboard/auth_trend.php. To get a sense of the jump, by April 2022
the number of Aadhaar authentications totalled 73.5 billion. Aadhaar
Dashboard data, April 2022, in https://uidai.gov.in/images/Aadhaar_
Brochure_July_22.pdf.

18. Sidhartha, 'UIDAI Pushes for Robust Authentication System', *The
Times of India*, 20 September 2022.

19. See the full text of PM Narendra Modi's speech on 15 August 2014,
available at https://www.narendramodi.in/pms-address-to-the-nation-
on-15th-august-6461; also see Nalin Mehta, 'Modi-Fied India: PM
Narendra Modi Scores from Red Fort', 15 August 2014, https://
timesofindia.indiatimes.com/blogs/academic-interest/modi-fied-india-
pm-narendra-modi-scores-from-red-fort/?source=app&frmapp=yes.

20. The full text of the speech is also available at https://indianexpress.
com/article/india/india-others/full-text-prime-minister-narendra-
modis-speech-on-68th-independence-day/.

21. PIB Delhi, Ministry of Finance, 'Pradhan Mantri Jan Dhan Yojana
(PMJDY) – National Mission for Financial Inclusion, Completes Eight
Years of Successful Implementation', 28 August 2022, https://www.
pib.gov.in/PressReleasePage.aspx?PRID=1854909; also see Yan Yan
Carriere-Swallow, V. Haksar and Manasa Patnam, 'India's Approach
to Open Banking: Some Implications for Financial Inclusion', IMF
Working Paper 2021/052, 26 February 2021, https://www.imf.org/
en/Publications/WP/Issues/2021/02/26/Indias-Approach-to-Open-
Banking-Some-Implications-for-Financial-Inclusion-50049;   Kevin
Lynch, 'India Makes Financial Record as Millions Open New Bank
Accounts', *Guinness World Records*, 20 January 2015, https://www.
guinnessworldrecords.com/news/2015/1/india-makes-financial-world-
record-as-millions-open-new-bank-accounts.

22. Claire Jones, 'India's Payments Revolution', *The Financial Times*,
16 December 2019, https://www.ft.com/content/27c94d40-5c6c-4af1-
ad40-c43b5cc691bd.

23. *The Economist*, 'India's Digital Platforms', https://www.economist.
com/special-report/2018/05/04/indias-digital-platforms?gclid=CjwKC
Ajw2OiaBhBSEiwAh2ZSPy-ajVRZnNmXQX_-Y0neplAgxvfbUuh3b
NJI3K6LocJA0s4taXPptRoCjfcQAvD_BwE&gclsrc=aw.ds.

24. Yan Yan Carriere-Swallow, V. Haksar and Manasa Patnam, 'India's
Approach to Open Banking: Some Implications for Financial

Inclusion', IMF Working Paper 2021/052, 26 February 2021, https://www.imf.org/en/Publications/WP/Issues/2021/02/26/Indias-Approach-to-Open-Banking-Some-Implications-for-Financial-Inclusion-50049, p. 9.

25. Ibid., p. 2.

26. Cristian Alonso, Tanuj Bhojwani, Emine Hanedar, Dinar Prihardini, Gerardo Uña and Kateryna Zhabska, 'Stacking Up the Benefits: Lessons from India's Digital Journey', IMF Working Paper 2023/078, 31 March 2023, https://www.imf.org/en/Publications/WP/Issues/2023/03/31/Stacking-up-the-Benefits-Lessons-from-Indias-Digital-Journey-531692, p. 1.

27. Derryl D'Silva, Zuzana Filkova, Frank Packer and Siddharth Tiwari, 'The Design of Digital Financial Infrastructure: Lessons from India', BIS Papers No. 106, 15 December 2019, Bank of International Settlements, https://www.bis.org/publ/bppdf/bispap106.htm, pp. 1–2.

28. Tiwari quoted in Claire Jones, 'India's Payments Revolution', *The Financial Times*, 16 December 2019, https://www.ft.com/content/27c94d40-5c6c-4af1-ad40-c43b5cc691bd.

29. Arvind Subramanian, *Of Counsel: The Challenges of the Modi-Jaitley Economy*, New Delhi: Penguin Random House, 2018, p. 225.

30. Ibid.

31. Ibid., pp. 225–26.

32. https://www.imf.org/external/pubs/ft/fandd/2021/07/india-stack-financial-access-and-digital-inclusion.htm.

33. Cristian Alonso, Tanuj Bhojwani, Emine Hanedar, Dinar Prihardini, Gerardo Uña and Kateryna Zhabska, 'Stacking Up the Benefits: Lessons from India's Digital Journey', IMF Working Paper 2023/078, 31 March 2023, https://www.imf.org/en/Publications/WP/Issues/2023/03/31/Stacking-up-the-Benefits-Lessons-from-Indias-Digital-Journey-531692, pp. 1–2.

34. Ashwini Vaishnaw's presentation at ET Global Summit, New Delhi, 18 February 2023; the full speech is available at https://economictimes.indiatimes.com/news/company/corporate-trends/etgbs-2023-india-is-investing-both-in-bricks-and-clicks-ashwini-vaishnaw/videoshow/98038219.cms.

35. Suraksha P., 'Seven Countries to Sign Up for India Stack's Digital Public Goods: MoS IT Rajeev Chandrasekhar', *The Economic Times*, 24 January 2023, https://economictimes.indiatimes.com/tech/

technology/seven-countries-to-sign-up-for-india-stacks-digital-public-goods-mos-it-rajeev-chandrasekhar/articleshow/97274552.cms?utm_source=contentofinterest&utm_medium=text&utm_campaign=cppst.

36. Arvind Gupta and Philip E. Auerswald, 'How India is Moving Towards a Digital-First Economy', *Harvard Business Review*, 8 November 2017, https://hbr.org/2017/11/how-india-is-moving-toward-a-digital-first-economy; Gupta at the time was CEO, MyGov India.

37. Ibid.

3. THE PLAY

1. Interview with Lakshmi and her son Sachin. Lakshmi spoke in Kannada, Sachin translated. Interview on videocall from Mandya, 5 November 2022. Lakshmi goes to a CSC each month to avail her widow pension. For another example of old pensions and their distribution through village-level entrepreneurs, see, for example, a case study from Angul, Odisha, in State Scan, 'VLE Sachin Disburses Old Age and Widow Pension Through DigiPay', *CSC Newsletter*, 3 February 2023, https://csc.gov.in/new_newsletter/2023/Feb/csc_newsletter_state_scan_3february_23.html.

2. 'Transactions Worth Rs 301.43 Crore Carried Out Under Digi Pay in March 2019', *CSC Newsletter*, https://csc.gov.in/new_newsletter/2019/May/csc_newsletter_highlight_7may_19.html; also see https://cscspv.in/financial-inclusion.html.

3. Interview with Rupesh Kumar, CSC Centre, Jhajhra, Dehradun, 2 November 2022. Also see https://csc.gov.in/.

4. Data from Parliamentary question response by Rajeev Chandrasekhar, minister of state for Electronics and Information Technology, in 'Common Services Centres Under CSC 2.0 Project', Unstarred Question no. 4680, Answered in Lok Sabha, 29 March 2023; data from https://csc.gov.in/, accessed 5 June 2023.

5. This was Rs 285,636.28 lakh transactions more than the previous year and with an incremental value of Rs 7,893.22 crore over the previous year. CSC: eGovernance Services Private Limited, *Annual Report 2020-21*, pp. 2, 50.

6. CSC: eGovernance Services Private Limited, *Annual Report 2020-21*, pp. 2, 50.

7. In the first phase of this, six of the state's then 29 districts were identified for the EBT pilot with smart cards. By March 2010, 3.5 lakh beneficiaries were enrolled for EBT in Karnataka. See, for example, BS Reporter, 'Banks Complete First Phase of Financial Inclusion', *Business Standard*, 23 October 2013, https://www.business-standard.com/article/finance/banks-complete-first-phase-of-financial-inclusion-113102301086_1.html; Special Correspondent, 'Speed Up EBT Scheme, Say Bankers', *The Hindu*, 8 May 2010, https://www.thehindu.com/news/national/karnataka/Speed-up-EBT-scheme-say-bankers/article16299162.ece.

8. According to Ministry of Finance data tabled in Parliament, as of 26 December 2018, 434 schemes of 56 ministries/departments had been onboarded onto the DBT portal. One example is the Ministry of Petroleum and Natural Gas's modified Direct Benefit Transfer (DBT) for LPG (DBTL/PAHAL) scheme launched in 54 districts on 15 November 2014 and across the country on 1 January 2015. LPG consumers who join the PAHAL scheme get the LPG cylinders at non-subsidised price and receive LPG subsidy (as per their entitlement) directly into their registered bank accounts. As on 27 March 2017, out of 19.81 crore active LPG consumers, 16.95 crore had joined the PAHAL scheme. Subsidy amount of more than Rs 46,000 crore had been transferred to the beneficiaries' bank accounts since its launch. A second example is that of MNREGA. As per NREGASoft, around 99 per cent of MNREGA wages were being paid electronically (FY 2018-19 as on 24 July 2018) into the Bank/Post Office accounts of MGNREGA workers through Electronic Fund Management System (eFMS). In FY 2013-14, only 37 per cent of the wages were paid electronically. Overall, DBT schemes include subsidies and benefits, such as scholarships, pension, wages and other social benefits under various Centrally Sponsored Schemes and Central Sector Schemes. Till 31 March 2017, Union government ministries reported savings of Rs 57,029 crore due to DBT. DBT data from P. Radhakrishnan, minister of state for Finance, Answer to Unstarred Question 2827, Lok Sabha, 28 December 2018, http://164.100.24.220/loksabhaquestions/annex/16/AU2827.pdf.

MNREGA details from Ram Kripal Yadav, minister of state for Rural Development, Answer to Lok Sabha Unstarred Question No. 1507, 26 July 2018, http://164.100.24.220/loksabhaquestions/

annex/15/AU1507.pdf. DBT savings estimate from P. Radhakrishnan, minister of state for Finance, Answer to Unstarred Question 18, Lok Sabha, 2 February 2018, http://164.100.24.220/loksabhaquestions/annex/14/AU18.pdf. LPG PAHAL data from Arjun Ram Meghwal, minister of state for Finance, Lok Sabha Unstarred Question 4922, 31 March 2017, http://164.100.24.220/loksabhaquestions/annex/11/AU4922.pdf.

9. This data tabled in Lok Sabha is available at http://164.100.24.220/loksabhaquestions/annex/174/AU1183.pdf and http://164.100.24.220/loksabhaquestions/annex/16/AU2827.pdf.

10. Spending on MGNREGS dropped in 2022-23 by 5 per cent to Rs 1.01 lakh crore. In FY 2023-24, the government hiked MGNREGS wages by 10 per cent from FY 2022-23 levels, but an analysis by *Business Standard* showed that in many states, wages remained lower than older rates, for various reasons. Analysis for FY 2022-23 from Banikinkar P., 'NREGS Spending Drops 5% in FY 23', *The Economic Times*, 7 April 2023. For analysis of MGNREGS spending in FY 2023-24, see the state-wise analysis by Sanjeeb Mukherjee, 'MNREGS Pay Still Below Minimum Wage in Several States, Shows Data', *Business Standard*, 27 March 2023.

11. The term was initially coined by the BJP, and political outreach to 'labharthee' groups became a crucial part of its mobilisation in the 2019 national elections. By 2023, opposition-led governments in the north Indian Hindi heartland were also using the term. For example, Rajasthan's Congress Chief Minister Ashok Gehlot organised a series of 'Labhathee Utsav' (Beneficiary Celebration) events in June 2023 to publicise DBT benefits to the poor from state government schemes. See, for example, Rajasthan government full-page advertisement on 'Labharthee Utsav' in *The Times of India*, 4 June 2023, p. 1.

12. Data from https://dbtbharat.gov.in/, accessed 29 May 2023.

13. From the highlights of PM Narendra Modi's speech, quoted in PIB, Prime Minister's Office, 'The Prime Minister, Shri Narendra Modi, Addressed the Nation from the Ramparts of the Red Fort on the 76th Independence Day', 15 August 2022, https://pib.gov.in/PressReleasePage.aspx?PRID=1852024.

14. PTI, 'Centre Saved $27 Billion in Schemes Using DBT Method: Economics Affairs Secy', *Business Standard*, 5 March 2023, https://www.business-standard.com/article/economy-policy/centre-

saved-27-bn-in-schemes-using-dbt-method-economic-affairs-secy-123030500400_1.html.

15. For example, although Narendra Modi remained India's most popular political leader by far, even in August 2021, the devastation caused by the pandemic was a big factor why *India Today*'s bi-annual 'Mood of the Nation' survey showed a comparative dip in his ratings, compared to the same period the previous year. When asked how they rated Modi's performance as prime minister, 54 per cent Indians rated it as 'good' or 'outstanding' in August 2021—down from 74 per cent in January 2021 and 78 per cent in August 2020. When asked who they thought was best suited to be India's next prime minister, 24 per cent still said Modi. In comparison, the highest rated opposition leader on this question was Rahul Gandhi, at 10 per cent. However, Modi's rating on this very question had fallen from 38 per cent in January 2021 and 66 per cent in August 2020. As the magazine's editorial director Raj Chengappa summed up, 'For Prime Minister Narendra Modi', the message coming out from this survey was clear: Indians were 'unhappy with the Centre's performance over the past six months' though they still 'saw the Modi government as the best bet' at the time. Subsequently, by January 2023, when asked again who they thought was best suited to be India's prime minister in 2024, 54 per cent of respondents in the same *India Today* 'Mood of the Nation' survey responded with Modi. His rating had clearly recovered. In comparison, in this survey, 14 per cent said Rahul Gandhi—after his Bharat Jodo Yatra. The bi-annual survey was conducted for *India Today* by Karvy Insights between 10 July and 20 July 2021, across 115 parliamentary and 230 assembly constituencies in 19 states. A total of 14,559 interviews were conducted—71 per cent in rural and 29 per cent in urban areas—with a mixed methodology—50 per cent face-to-face and 50 per cent telephonic interviews—adopted due to COVID-related restrictions. *India Today*, 'India Today Mood of the Nation Survey', August 2021, https://www.indiatoday.in/mood-of-the-nation-survey-august-2021; Raj Chengappa, 'Motion Poll: Economy the Big Worry', *India Today*, 16 August 2021, https://www.indiatoday.in/magazine/cover-story/story/20210823-mood-of-the-nation-poll-economy-the-big-worry-1841399-2021-08-16.

16. During the COVID-19 lockdown, more than Rs 36,659 crore (Rs 27,442 crores [Centrally sponsored Scheme CSS+ Central Sector

Schemes (CS)] + Rs 9,717 [State Government]) were transferred by using Direct Benefit Transfer through Public Financial Management System (PFMS) into bank accounts of 16.01 crore beneficiaries (11.42 crores [CSS/CS] + 4.59 crores [State]) during COVID-19 lockdown by the Controller General of Accounts (CGA) office, Department of Expenditure, Ministry of Finance. Data is for 24 March 2020 till 17 April 2020. This was for schemes like PM KISAN, Mahatma Gandhi National Employment Guarantee Scheme (MNREGS), National Social Assistance Programme (NSAP), Prime Minister's Matru Vandana Yojana (PMMVY), National Rural Livelihood Mission (NRLM), National Health Mission (NHM) and scholarship schemes of various ministries through National Scholarship Portal (NSP).

Payments were also made under the PM Garib Kalyan Yojana. Rs 500 was credited in the women account holder of Jan Dhan accounts. Till 13 April 2020, the total number of women beneficiaries were 19.86 crore, which resulted in disbursement of Rs 9,930 crore (as per data of Department of Financial Services).

Between 24 March 2020 and 17 April 2020, through 180 welfare schemes, the state governments used PFMS to disburse an amount of Rs 9,217.22 crore to 45,903,908 beneficiaries.

PIB, Ministry of Finance, 'More Than Rs 36,659 Crore Transferred by Using Direct Benefit Transfer (DBT) through Public Financial Management System (PFMS) in the Bank accounts of 16.01 Crore Beneficiaries during COVID-19 Lockdown', 19 April 2020, https://pib.gov.in/Pressreleaseshare.aspx?PRID=1616022.

17. See, for example, Nalin Mehta, 'The BJP Has Changed the Old Rules of Politics', *The Hindustan Times*, 10 March 2022, https://www.hindustantimes.com/opinion/the-bjp-has-changed-the-old-rules-of-politics-101646930084101.html; Nalin Mehta, 'How Yogi's Unbeatable Model of Hindutva + Welfare + Development Won UP', *The Times of India*, 13 March 2022, https://timesofindia.indiatimes.com/india/how-the-unbeatable-combo-of-hindutva-welfare-development-won-up/articleshow/90168840.cms.

18. Nalin Mehta, 'Gujarat Verdict: The Story Behind Making History – The BJP's Record Victory Was Based on an Expansion of Geographical Base and Social Blocs', *The Times of India*, 8 December 2022, https://timesofindia.indiatimes.com/blogs/academic-interest/gujarat-verdict-

the-story-behind-making-history-bjps-record-victory-was-built-on-an-expansion-of-geographical-base-and-social-blocs/.

19. See, for example, Nalin Mehta, 'CongNataka: Local Pitch, Rural Vote Script Win', *The Times of India*, 14 May 2023, https://timesofindia.indiatimes.com/blogs/academic-interest/congnataka-local-pitch-rural-vote-script-win-2/.

20. PM Narendra Modi speaking at ET Global Business Summit 2023, 23 February 2023. See full speech at https://www.youtube.com/watch?v=ePZuZSUWNHc.

21. Available at Chrome-extension://efaidnbmnnnibpcajpcglclefindmkaj/http://164.100.24.220/loksabhaquestions/annex/178/AU4448.pdf.

22. Interview with Saurabh Kumar, director, Ministry of Finance, New Delhi, 6 April 2022. Kumar was private secretary (2019–21) and additional private secretary (2014–19) to minister for Communication and IT and Law and Justice Communications. He was additional commissioner, GST, at the time of the interview.

23. Data from https://transformingindia.mygov.in/performance-dashboard/#primary, data is accurate as of 30 May 2023; PIB, Ministry of Electronics & IT, 'Provision of Cyber Services through CSCs in Gram Panchayats', 5 August 2022, https://pib.gov.in/PressReleasePage.aspx?PRID=1848733.

24. CSC: eGovernance Services Private Limited, *Annual Report 2020-21*, p. 8.

25. Interview with Neeraj Singh, 30 October 2022.

26. Information from https://register.csc.gov.in/page/faq.

27. Data from Common Service Centre (CSC), Ministry of Electronics and Information Technology, https://csc.gov.in/vle.

28. Interview with Jitendra Sachdev, CSC Centre, Prem Nagar, Dehradun, 1 November 2022.

29. Sundar Pichai's interview with Surabhi Agarwal, Aashish Aryan and Bodhistava Ganguly, in 'Country Has Set Shining Example with UPI, Aadhaar & India Stack' and 'Google Wants to be a Responsible Local Firm, Aid Digital India Vision', *The Economic Times*, 21 December 2022, pp. 1, 10.

30. Satya Nadella, CEO, Microsoft, in conversation with Nandan Nilekani, see clip at https://www.youtube.com/watch?v=NOwDsgardpo; also see Sai Ishwarbarath, 'India Showing the World How Tech Can Enable Inclusivity: Microsoft CEO Satya Nadella', *The Economic*

Times, 6 January 2023, https://economictimes.indiatimes.com/tech/ technology/india-is-showing-the-world-on-how-tech-can-enable-inclusivity-microsoft-ceo-satya-nadella/articleshow/96767222.cms; Surabhi Agarwal, ET Bureau, 'Digital India and India Stack Have Made the Country Stand Out: Satya Nadella', *The Economic Times*, 17 December 2020, https://economictimes.indiatimes.com/tech/ technology/digital-india-and-india-stack-have-made-the-country-stand-out-satya-nadella/articleshow/79783076.cms.

31. Bill Gates, Fifth RNG Lecture, 'India is Not Just a Beneficiary of New Breakthroughs, but an Innovator of Them', *The Indian Express*, 3 March 2023, https://indianexpress.com/article/india/bill-gates-india-is-not-just-a-beneficiary-of-new-breakthroughs-but-an-innovator-of-them-8476560/.

32. Our Bureau, 'India's Direct Benefit Transfer Scheme is a Logistical Marvel: IMF', *The Economic Times*, 14 October 2022, https:// economictimes.indiatimes.com/news/economy/finance/indias-direct-benefit-transfer-scheme-is-a-logistical-marvel-imf-paola-mauro/ articleshow/94845594.cms.

33. Quoted in IMF Managing Director Kristalina Georgieva's interview with Sruthijit K.K. and Gireesh Chandra Prasad, 'India Gained from Right Targeting, Digitalization: IMF MD Kristalina Georgieva', *Mint*, 12 September 2022, https://www.livemint.com/politics/ news/india-gained-from-right-targeting-digitalization-kristalina-georgieva-11662922844697.html.

34. Our Bureau, 'India's Direct Benefit Transfer Scheme Is a Logistical Marvel: IMF', *The Economic Times*, 14 October 2022, https:// economictimes.indiatimes.com/news/economy/finance/indias-direct-benefit-transfer-scheme-is-a-logistical-marvel-imf-paola-mauro/ articleshow/94845594.cms.

35. https://twitter.com/COdendahl/status/1565071721572536321?s=20.

36. ETEch, 'Germany's Struggles with ePay Make Aadhaar, UPI Real Heroes', *The Economic Times*, 2 September 2022, https://economictimes. indiatimes.com/tech/trendspotting/germanys-struggles-with-epay-make-aadhaar-upi-real-heroes/articleshow/93935109.cms?utm_ source=contentofinterest&utm_medium=text&utm_campaign=cppst.

4.   IMPACT

1.   The Swachh Bharat Mission was launched on 2 October 2014, Gandhi's birthday, by modifying the UPA government's erstwhile Nirmal Bharat Abhiyan, and putting in place a five-year target. The scheme increased allocation for individual household toilets to Rs 12,000 from Rs 10,000. Of this, the Union government's share of funding was 60 per cent (Rs 7,200 per toilet), while the state governments' share was 40 per cent (Rs 4,800 per toilet). For states in the Northeast, Jammu and Kashmir and Special Category States, the Centre–state ratio of funding was 90 per cent (Rs 10,800 per toilet): 10 per cent (Rs 1,200 per toilet). Details from Swachh Bharat Mission, 'FAQs— SBM Phase I', https://swachhbharatmission.gov.in/SBMCMS/faq. htm, and Swachh Bharat Mission, Guidelines for Swachh Bharat Mission (Gramin), revised October 2017, p. 17, available at https:// swachhbharatmission.gov.in/SBMCMS/writereaddata/portal/images/ pdf/sbm-ph-II-Guidelines.pdf.

2.   Indira Awas Yojana was restructured into PMAY-G with effect from 1 April 2016—and the revised scheme formally launched on 20 November 2016—with an initial target of building 1 crore pucca house by 2018-19, with a final end-target of 2022. Aimed at providing pucca housing to all, the scheme increased unit assistance from Rs 70,000 to Rs 1.2 lakh per beneficiary in the plains and from Rs 75,000 to Rs 1.3 lakh in hilly states, difficult areas and Integrated Action Plan (IAP) districts. The beneficiary is entitled to 90 to 95 person days of unskilled labour from MGNREGS. The scheme is administered by the Ministry of Rural Development. Separately, the Pradhan Mantri Awas Yojana-Urban (PMAY-U) is administered by the Ministry of Housing and Urban Affairs. PMAY-U was launched on 25 June 2015 and focuses on 'urban housing shortage among the EWS/LIG and MIG categories including the slum dwellers by ensuring a pucca house to all eligible urban households by the year 2022'. Essentially, in operational terms, they are separate schemes— one rural, one urban—run by two different ministries with different reporting lines and administrative hierarchies but both fall within the broad rubric of the Modi's government's 'Housing for All' Mission. For PMAY-G, see https://pmayg.nic.in/netiay/about.aspx; PIB, Ministry of Rural Development, 'PM Launches "Housing for All" in Rural

Areas', 20 November 2016, https://pib.gov.in/newsite/printrelease. aspx?relid=153931. For PMAY-U, see details on https://pmaymis.gov. in/; Pradhan Mantri Awas Yojana, *Housing for All (Urban)-Scheme Guidelines 2015* (New Delhi: Ministry of Housing and Urban Poverty Alleviation, 2015) and Kaushal Kishore, minister of state for Housing and Urban Affairs, in response to Lok Sabha Unstarred Question No. 1827, answered on 29 July 2021.

3. Interview with Hemant Chouhan, gram pradhan, Shahpur Bans Must village, Saharanpur district, UP, 17 June 2020.

4. This point was made to me by the journalist Brijesh Shukla. Interview with Brijesh Shukla, columnist, *Navbharat Times*, Lucknow, 11 June 2020.

5. See, for example, the *Indian Express* investigation into an irrigation scam in Jharkhand where Aadhaar cards were misused: Abhishek Anand, 'Irrigation Scam Unravels in Jharkhand: Aadhaar Misused, Funds Claimed, Farmers Clueless', *The Indian Express*, 9 June 2023, https://indianexpress.com/article/express-exclusive/express-investigation-irrigation-scheme-unravels-in-jharkhand-aadhaar-misused-funds-claimed-farmers-clueless-8653463/.

6. Brijesh Shukla. Interview with Brijesh Shukla, columnist, *Navbharat Times*, Lucknow, 11 June 2020.

7. Ashwani Kumar, 'Is Cash Transfer a "Congress Calling Card"?', *Business Standard*, 29 January 2013, https://www.business-standard. com/article/opinion/ashwani-kumar-is-cash-transfer-a-congress-calling-card-113010200040_1.html.

8. See, for example, Saba Naqvi, 'Freshly Minted Cheer', *Outlook*, 10 December 2012, https://www.outlookindia.com/magazine/story/ freshly-minted-cheer/283179.

9. The UPA government initiated DBT with effect from 1 January 2013 in 43 identified districts for 24 selected schemes. The NDA government (vide O.M. No. I-11011/58/2013-DBT dated 13 February 2015 and 19 February 2015 expanded the scope of DBT to cover all Central Sector Schemes/Centrally Sponsored Schemes in which cash benefits are transferred to individual beneficiaries. Source: Jayant Singh, minister of state for Finance, answer to Lok Sabha Unstarred Question No. 2077, 6 May 2016.

10. RBI gave approval to banks for e-KYC verification through Aadhaar only on 2 September 2013 vide RBI/2013-14/209. DBOD.AML.

BC.No.44/14.01.001/2013-14, https://www.rbi.org.in/scripts/NotificationUser.aspx?Id=8357&Mode=0.

11. Conversation with a senior government official, with knowledge of the matter, speaking on condition of anonymity, 6 April 2022.

12. The Election Commission of India (ECI) allowed the Union Agriculture Ministry to transfer the first and second tranches of the payment to all those beneficiaries registered under the scheme before 10 March 2019. Ahead of the Lok Sabha polls, the Centre announced the Rs 75,000-crore Pradhan Mantri Kisan Samman Nidhi (PM-Kisan) scheme under which Rs 6,000 per year would be disbursed in three instalments to around 12 crore farmers who hold cultivable land up to two hectares. PTI, 'PM Kisan Scheme: 4.74 Crore Farmers to Get Second Instalment from Next Month', *The Economic Times*, 23 March 2019, https://economictimes.indiatimes.com/news/economy/policy/pm-kisan-scheme-about-4-74-crore-farmers-to-get-second-installment-from-next-month/articleshow/68535847.cms.

13. Available at chrome-extension://efaidnbmnnnibpcajpcglclefindmkaj/https://pqals.nic.in/annex/1711/AU2124.pdf.

14. Narendra Modi speech in Kannauj, 26 April 2019, available at Narendra Modi YouTube channel, https://www.youtube.com/watch?v=JCSMN_ju7YE&feature=emb_logo.

15. Minister for Agriculture and Farmers Welfare Narendra Singh Tomar, Government of India, Ministry of Agriculture and Farmers Welfare, Department of Agriculture and Farmers Welfare, Lok Sabha Unstarred Question No. 3313, answered on 21 March 2023; chrome-extension://efaidnbmnnnibpcajpcglclefindmkaj/https://pqals.nic.in/annex/1711/AU3313.pdf https://transformingindia.mygov.in/performance-dashboard/#primary.

16. BRS was earlier Telangana Rashtriya Samithi (TRS). Formed in 2001 as TRS, it received approval from the ECI for its rechristening on 8 December 2022, after the party passed a resolution for name-change on 5 October 2022 and formally asked the ECI for a name-change. Koride Mahesh, TNN, 'TRS Becomes BRS: ECI Approves Party's Name Change', *The Times of India*, 8 December 2022, https://timesofindia.indiatimes.com/city/hyderabad/trs-becomes-brs-eci-approves-party-name-change/articleshow/96088930.cms.

17. Details from http://rythubandhu.telangana.gov.in/Default_RB1.aspx.

18. The Rythu Bandhu programme reaches 57,15,870 farmers across 32 Telangana districts at the time. For details, see http://rythubandhu. telangana.gov.in/Default_RB1.aspx; implementation details from Government of Telangana, Agriculture and Cooperation Department, *Guidelines for Implementation of Agriculture Investment Support Scheme ('Rythu Bandhu') in Telangana State-Orders Issued*, G.O. Rt. No 231, 4 April 2018. For a critical analysis, see Sai Manish, 'Winning Elections Telangana Style: Pay Farm Land Owners, Ignore the Tillers', *Business Standard*, 20 December 2018, https://www.business-standard. com/article/current-affairs/winning-elections-telangana-style-pay-farm-landowners-ignore-the-tillers-118122000386_1.html. For detailed analysis, also see, for instance, the case study by Abhishek Shaw, Sawan Rathi and Anindya S. Chakrabarti, 'Land-holding Inequality and Responses to Government Interventions', Indian Institute of Management Ahmedabad CPHS Research Seminar Series, 19 January 2023. Also see the case study by Susan Thomas, Diya Uday and Bhargavi Zaveri, *Linking Welfare Distribution to Land Records: A Case-study of the Rythu Bandhu Scheme (RBS) in Telangana*, Indira Gandhi Institute of Development Research, 2020, TR-2020-4-27. Available at https://ruralindiaonline.org/en/library/resource/linking-welfare-distribution-to-land-records-rythu-bandhu-scheme-in-telangana/.

19. Quoted in Nalin Mehta and Sanjeev Singh's interview with K.T. Rama Rao in Hyderabad, for 'Election with Times', *The Times of India*, 30 November 2018.

20. Ibid. K.T. Ram Rao repeated the sentiment later at the state government's Rythu Bandhu celebrations in 2022. Special Correspondent, 'Rythu Bandhu a Revolutionary Scheme Shielding Farmers, Says KTR', *The Hindu*, 10 January 2022, https://www.thehindu.com/news/national/telangana/rythu-bandhu-a-revolutionary-scheme-shielding-farmers-says-ktr/article38220432.ece.

21. Ayesha Minhaz, 'Rythu Bandhu: A Lifeline for Farmers in Telangana', *Frontline*, 9 March 2023, https://frontline.thehindu.com/the-nation/agriculture/rythu-bandhu-scheme-in-telangana-a-success-but-more-needs-to-be-done/article66571551.ece.

22. http://rythubandhu.telangana.gov.in/Default_RB1.aspx.

23. Ibid.

24. Ayesha Minhaz, 'Rythu Bandhu: A Lifeline for Farmers in Telangana', *Frontline*, 9 March 2023, https://frontline.thehindu.com/the-nation/

agriculture/rythu-bandhu-scheme-in-telangana-a-success-but-more-needs-to-be-done/article66571551.ece.

25. Ibid.

26. Congress, 'Congress Schemes Repackaged/Renamed by NDA', https://www.inc.in/en/congress-schemes-renamed-by-bjp.

27. Neelanjan Sircar, 'The Politics of Vishwas: Political Mobilization in the 2019 National Election', *Contemporary South Asia*, Vol. 28, No. 2, 26 May 2020, pp. 178–94, https://doi.org/10.1080/09584935.2020.1765988. Also see Christophe Jaffrelot and Gilles Verniers, 'The BJP's 2019 Election Campaign: Not Business as Usual', *Contemporary South Asia*, Vol. 28, No. 2, 18 May 2020, pp. 155–77, https://doi.org/10.1080/09584935.2020.1765985; Christophe Jaffrelot, 'Class and Caste in the 2019 Indian Election–Why Have So Many Poor Started Voting for Modi?' *Studies in Indians Politics*, Vol. 7, No. 2, 1 December 2019, pp. 149–60, https://doi.org/10.1177/2321023019874890, first published online on 12 November 2019; Rajeshwari Deshpande, Louise Tillin and K.K. Kailash, 'The BJP's Welfare Schemes: Did They Make a Difference in the 2019 Elections?' *Studies in Indian Politics*, Vol. 7, No. 2, November 2019, pp. 219–33, https://doi.org/10.1177/2321023019874911.

28. Yamini Aiyar, 'Modi Consolidates Power: Leveraging Welfare Politics', *Journal of Democracy*, Vol. 30, No. 4, p. 84.

29. Anant Zanane, 'Akhilesh Yadav's Free Laptops for Students Boot Up With Mulayam Photo', NDTV, 11 March 2013, https://www.ndtv.com/india-news/akhilesh-yadavs-free-laptops-for-students-boot-up-with-mulayam-photo-515845; Agencies, 'UP CM Akhilesh Yadav Launches Free Laptop Scheme for Students', *The Economic Times*, 11 March 2013, https://economictimes.indiatimes.com/nation-world/up-cm-akhilesh-yadav-launches-free-laptop-scheme-for-students/laptop-bags-have-images-of-yadav-his-father/slideshow/18923275.cms.

30. Priyangi Aggarwal, 'UP Begins Distributing School Bags with Pictures of Former CM Akhilesh Yadav', *The Economic Times*, 21 April 2017, https://economictimes.indiatimes.com/news/politics-and-nation/up-begins-distributing-school-bags-with-pictures-of-former-cm-akhilesh-yadav/articleshow/58294440.cms?from=mdr; HT Correspondent, 'Schoolkids to Get Bags with Akhilesh Photo', *Hindustan Times*, 3 March 2017, https://www.hindustantimes.com/lucknow/schoolkids-

to-get-bags-with-akhilesh-photo/story-QYgzNo03aO91FU3dG72IUJ.
html.

31. Arun Janardhan, 'Tamil Nadu Budget 2023: Govt to Roll Out Much-
awaited Rs 1,000 Monthly Aid for Women Homemakers', *The Indian
Express*, 21 March 2023, https://indianexpress.com/article/cities/
chennai/tamil-nadu-budget-2023-govt-roll-out-monthly-aid-women-
homemakers-8507752/.

32. The Hindu Bureau, 'TN Budget: Scheme for ₹1,000 Cash
Assistance for Eligible Women Heads of Families, to be Launched
on September 15', *The Hindu*, 20 March 2023, https://www.thehindu.
com/news/national/tamil-nadu/tn-budget-scheme-for-1000-cash-
assistance-for-eligible-women-heads-of-families-to-be-launched-on-
september-15/article66641142.ece.

33. Debashish Konar, TNN, 'Bengal Govt to Include all Women Aged
25 to 60 in Income Scheme', *The Times of India*, https://timesofindia.
indiatimes.com/city/kolkata/bengal-govt-to-include-all-women-aged-
25-to-60-in-income-scheme/articleshow/85441911.cms; ABP News
Bureau, 'Mamata Banerjee Announces Rs 12,000 Cr Women Cash
Scheme: All You Need to Know', *ABP*, 23 July 2021, https://news.
abplive.com/news/india/mamata-banerjee-announces-rs-12-000-cr-
women-cash-scheme-all-you-need-to-know-1471605.

34. DBT Mission, DBT Performance Ranking of States/UTs, chrome-
extension://efaidnbmnnnibpcajpcglclefindmkaj/https://dbtbharat.gov.
in/documents/ranking/State-Ranking.pdf.

35. Data from Swachh Bharat Mission Gramin Dashboard, 27 November
2020, https://sbm.gov.in/sbmdashboard/IHHL.aspx.

36. Narendra Modi's speech in Kannauj, 26 April 2019, available at
Narendra Modi YouTube channel, https://www.youtube.com/
watch?v=JCSMN_ju7YE&feature=emb_logo.

37. 18 April 2023 data from PM Awas Dashboard, https://dashboard.rural.
nic.in/dashboardnew/pmayg.aspx; December 2021 data from https://
pib.gov.in/PressReleaseIframePage.aspx?PRID=1781441; https://pib.
gov.in/PressReleasePage.aspx?PRID=1773447.

38. 18 April 2023 data from PM Awas Dashboard, https://dashboard.
rural.nic.in/dashboardnew/pmayg.aspx; December 2021 data from
https://pib.gov.in/PressReleaseIframePage.aspx?PRID=1781441;
data from PM Awas Yojana–Gramin, Awassoft Dashboard, 'C2-
Category-wise Houses Sanctioned and Completed', 27 November

2020, https://rhreporting.nic.in/netiay/SocialProgressReport/ Categorywisehousescompletedreport.aspx.

39. April 2023 data from https://dashboard.rural.nic.in/dashboardnew/ pmayg.aspx; for earlier data, 2018–21, see https://pib.gov.in/PressRelease IframePage.aspx?PRID=1781441.

40. The Centre–state funding ratio is 90:10 in the Northeast and Himalayan states, https://pmayg.nic.in/netiay/about.aspx. Also see PMAY-G, Ministry of Rural Development, *Framework for Implementation— Pradhan Mantri Awas Yojana Gramin*, available at https://pmayg.nic. in/netiay/Uploaded/English_Book_Final.pdf.

41. PM Awas Yojana-Gramin MIS, 'C.1 Gender-wise Houses Sanctioned and Completed', 18 April 2023, https://rhreporting.nic.in/netiay/ SocialProgressReport/Ownershipdetailsofhousessanctionedreport. aspx 24/10/2020. Also see NIPFP Research Team, *Evaluation of Governance Parameters of Pradhan Mantri Awaas Yojana-Gramin (PMAY-G) Third Report Submitted to Ministry of Rural Development Government of India* (New Delhi: National Institute of Public Finance and Policy, December 2019), p. 87.

42. Full text of Narendra Modi's live address and interaction with the Karnataka BJP Mahila Morcha, 4 May 2018, https://www.narendramodi. in/country-is-moving-towards-women-led-development-539996. The text is in Hindi and the translations are by the author. Also see PTI, 'PMAY-Urban: Registration to Include Woman's Name Mandatorily', *The Financial Express*, 30 May 2016, https://www.financialexpress. com/economy/pmay-urban-registeration-to-include-womans-name-mandatorily/269459/.

43. Apurva Viswanath, 'Explained: Reading SC's Verdict on Hindu Women's Inheritance Rights', *The Indian Express*, 17 August 2020, https://indianexpress.com/article/explained/reading-supreme-court-verdict-on-hindu-womens-inheritance-rights-6550767/.

44. PM Awas Yojana-Gramin MIS, 'C.1 Gender-wise Houses Sanctioned and Completed', 18 April 2023, https://rhreporting.nic.in/netiay/ SocialProgressReport/Ownershipdetailsofhousessanctionedreport. aspx 24/10/2020. Also see NIPFP Research Team, *Evaluation of Governance Parameters of Pradhan Mantri Awaas Yojana-Gramin (PMAY-G) Third Report Submitted to Ministry of Rural Development Government of India* (New Delhi: National Institute of Public Finance and Policy, December 2019), p. 87.

45. In Bihar, women-only or joint-women-ownership houses built under the scheme amounted to 30,20,174; in MP: 23,47,248; Rajasthan: 12,32,380; in UP: 25,53,367 houses. PM Awas Yojana-Gramin MIS, 'C.1 Gender-wise Houses Sanctioned and Completed', 18 April 2023, https://rhreporting.nic.in/netiay/SocialProgressReport/Ownershipdetailsofhousessanctionedreport.aspx 18/04/2023.

46. Additional data from minister for Rural Development Narendra Singh Tomar, Answer to Lok Sabha Unstarred Question No. 1936, 3 March 2020, http://164.100.24.220/loksabhaquestions/annex/173/AU1936.pdf; Ram Kripal Yadav, minister of state for Rural Development, Answer to Lok Sabha Unstarred Question No. 1061, 8 February 2018, http://164.100.24.220/loksabhaquestions/annex/14/AU1061.pdf and Answer to Lok Sabha Unstarred Question No. 1337, 9 February 2017, http://164.100.24.220/loksabhaquestions/annex/11/AU1337.pdf; Narendra Singh Tomar, minister for Rural Development, Answer to Lok Sabha Unstarred Question No. 414, 19 November 2019, http://164.100.24.220/loksabhaquestions/annex/172/AU414.pdf.

47. Interview with a senior official in the UP Chief Minister's Office (CMO), Lucknow, 9 June 2020.

48. Ibid.

49. Aman Sharma, 'In Stance Shift, Congress Adopts Aadhaar in Madhya Pradesh', The Economic Times, 11 January 2019, https://economictimes.indiatimes.com/news/politics-and-nation/in-stance-shift-congress-adopts-aadhaar-in-madhya-pradesh/articleshow/67480516.cms?from=mdr.

50. https://twitter.com/chetan_bhagat/status/1391635654069653505?s=20.

51. PM Narendra Modi's address to the nation on 22 October 2021, available at Narendra Modi YouTube channel, https://www.youtube.com/watch?v=L9bTUczQA6w.

52. PIB, Ministry of Health and Family Welfare, 'India Achieves Major Landmark of "200 Crore" COVID-19 Vaccinations', 17 July 2022, https://pib.gov.in/PressReleasePage.aspx?PRID=1842157.

53. PIB, Prime Minister's Office, 'PM Meets Bill Gates', 4 March 2023, https://pib.gov.in/PressReleasePage.aspx?PRID=1904126.

54. S. Jaishankar's video clip tweeted by Norwegian diplomat and former minister Erik Solheim, available at https://twitter.com/ErikSolheim/status/1559361552100167680?s=20.

55. Money Control News, 'When S Jaishankar and His Son Went to a US Restaurant This Happened', Moneycontrol.com, 17 August 2022, https://www.moneycontrol.com/news/trends/viral-video-when-s-jaishankar-and-son-went-to-a-us-restaurant-this-happened-9044701.html.

56. https://twitter.com/Pawankhera/status/1530142972091588609?t=pP3U3D18n8sdD00S0HTIzg&s=08.

57. https://twitter.com/buzzindelhi/status/1548601003368665088?s=20.

58. PIB, Ministry of Finance, 'More than Rs 36,659 Crore Transferred by Using Direct Benefit Transfer (DBT) through Public Financial Management System (PFMS) in the Bank Accounts of 16.01 crore Beneficiaries during COVID 2019 Lockdown', 17 April 2020, https://pib.gov.in/Pressreleaseshare.aspx?PRID=1616022.

59. Editorial, 'Why the Centre Is Right in Not Extending the Pradhan Mantri Garib Kalyan Anna Yojana', *The Indian Express*, 26 December 2022, https://indianexpress.com/article/opinion/editorials/why-the-centre-is-right-in-not-extending-the-pradhan-mantri-garib-kalyan-anna-yojana-scheme-8343812/.

60. PIB, Cabinet, 'Centre Extends Pradhan Mantri Garib Kalyan Ann Yojana (PMGKAY) for Another Three Months (October 2022–December 2022)', 28 September 2022, https://pib.gov.in/PressReleasePage.aspx?PRID=1862944.

61. Aftab Ahmad and Rajendra Jadhav, 'India Replaces COVID-era Food Programme with Cheaper Scheme', *Reuters*, 23 December 2022, https://www.reuters.com/world/india/india-says-provide-free-food-grains-poor-one-year-2022-12-23/.

62. BJP, 'Mujhe Chalte Jaana Hai', video released on 14 March 2023, available at https://youtu.be/jFBhu7c6XmM.

5. THE HINGES

1. NPCI, 1 June 2023, https://twitter.com/NPCI_NPCI/status/ 1664213042450792450?s=20.

2. MyGovIndia, 9 June 2023, https://twitter.com/mygovindia/status/1667207266888740864?s=20.

3. Anand Adhikari, 'The Giant Killer', *Business Today*, 15 September 2022, https://www.businesstoday.in/interactive/longread/upi-the-made-in-india-payments-system-is-rocking-not-just-india-but-is-making-waves-globally-too-171-15-09-2022.

4. Ramesh Narasimhan, CEO of Worldline India, quoted in ibid.

5. Pranav Mukul, 'Explained: How Indians Now Make Payments Using UPI in UAE', *The Indian Express*, 23 April 2022, https://indianexpress. com/article/explained/explained-indians-payments-upi-uae-7881510/.

6. Traditionally, the most preferred method of UPI transactions is linking the bank account in any UPI-enabled app for making payments. This contributes over 99.9 per cent of total UPI transactions. These bank account-to-account transactions remained free for customers and merchants until the time of writing in June 2023. However, with new regulatory guidelines, Prepaid Payment Instruments (PPI Wallets) were permitted to be part of interoperable UPI ecosystem. From 1 April 2023, certain categories of these PPI merchant transactions above Rs 2,000 were to be charged at 1.1 per cent, with no charge to customers. For details, see the National Payments Corporation of India (NPCI) statement on 29 March 2023, https://twitter.com/ NPCI_NPCI/status/1640964585267281926?s=20; also see Anulekha Ray, 'Which UPI Payments Will Attract Interchange Fee? Will You Have to Bear the Cost?' *The Economic Times*, 18 April 2023, https://economictimes.indiatimes.com/wealth/spend/upi-merchant-transactions-ppi-which-upi-payments-will-attract-interchange-fee-will-you-have-to-bear-the-cost/articleshow/99087712.cms.

7. This formulation is from Seema Sirohi, 'Exporting Digital India', *The Economic Times*, 27 October 2022, p. 10.

8. Full text of Ambedkar's thesis is available in Vasant moon (ed.), *Dr. Babasaheb Ambedkar Writings and Speeches Vol. 12* (First Edition by Education Department, Govt. of Maharashtra, 14 April 1993; reprinted by Dr. Ambedkar Foundation, January 2014). Available at https://mea.gov.in/Images/attach/amb/Volume_12.pdf.

9. The full text of Ambedkar's thesis is available at https://www. roundtableindia.co.in/the-problem-of-the-rupee-its-origin-and-its-solution-history-of-indian-currency-a-banking/.

10. For more on Ambedkar's economic ideas, see S. Ambirajan, 'Ambedkar's Contributions to Indian Economics', *Economic and Political Weekly*, Vol. 34, No. 46/47, 20–26 November 1999, pp. 3280–5; Narendra Jadhav, 'Neglected Economic Thought of Babasaheb Ambedkar', *Economic and Political Weekly*, Vol. 26, No. 15, 13 April 1991, pp. 980–2.

11. Full speech available at https://www.narendramodi.in/text-of-pms-speech-at-digidhan-mela-in-new-delhi-s-talkatora-stadium-30-december-2016-533672.
12. Ibid.
13. Full text of Modi's demonetisation speech available at https://pib.gov.in/newsite/PrintRelease.aspx?relid=153404.
14. PIB, Ministry of Drinking Water and Sanitation, 'BHIM Will Create Equality', 3 January 2017, https://pib.gov.in/PressReleasePage.aspx?PRID=1479881.
15. PTI, 'Chidambaram Slams Modi Government's "Terrible" Demonetisation Decision', *National Herald*, 9 February 2017, https://www.nationalheraldindia.com/news/former-finance-minister-p-chidambaram-in-rajya-sabha-note-ban-most-terrible-decision-of-modi-government.
16. Ibid.
17 Tom Groenfeldt, 'DBS CEO Sees Bright Future for Asia – Others See Some Problems', *Forbes*, 12 October 2015, https://www.forbes.com/sites/tomgroenfeldt/2015/10/12/dbs-ceo-sees-bright-future-for-asia-others-see-some-problems/?sh=79e37b28381f.
18. Quoted in *The Economist*, 'Who Gains and Who Loses from Some Financial Inclusion', 4 May 2018, https://www.economist.com/special-report/2018/05/04/who-gains-and-who-loses-from-more-financial-inclusion.
19. *The Economist*, 'In Bleak Times for Banks, India's Digital Payments System Wins Praise', 9 May 2020, https://www.economist.com/finance-and-economics/2020/05/09/in-bleak-times-for-banks-indias-digital-payments-system-wins-praise.
20. NPCI, https://www.npci.org.in/who-we-are/about-us.
21. Claire Jones, 'India's Payments Revolution', *The Financial Times*, 16 December 2019, https://www.ft.com/content/27c94d40-5c6c-4af1-ad40-c43b5cc691bd.
22. US Federal Reserve, 'Federal Reserve Announces July Launch for the FedNow Service', 15 March 2023, https://www.federalreserve.gov/newsevents/pressreleases/other20230315a.htm.
23. Charles Birnkaum and Eric Kaplan, 'How FedNow and Faster Payments Will Impact Fintech', Bessemer Venture Partners, 1 June 2023, https://www.bvp.com/atlas/how-fednow-and-faster-payments-will-impact-u-s-fintech.

24. Data from NCPI, accurate as of August 2022. Quoted in Digbijay Mishra and Tarush Bhalla, 'NPCI Pings Govt, Industry on UPI Market Share', *The Economic Times*, 20 September 2022, https://economictimes. indiatimes.com/tech/technology/npci-pings-govt-industry-on-upi-market-share-cap/articleshow/94310588.cms?from=mdr.

25. *The Economist*, 'In Bleak Times for Banks, India's Digital Payments System Wins Praise', 9 May 2020, https://www.economist.com/finance-and-economics/2020/05/09/in-bleak-times-for-banks-indias-digital-payments-system-wins-praise.

26. Committee on Payments and Market Infrastructures, Bank of International Settlements, World Bank Group, Payment Aspects of Financial Inclusion in the Fintech Era, April 2020, p. 18, https://www.bis.org/cpmi/publ/d191.pdf.

27. Claire Jones, 'India's Payments Revolution', *The Financial Times*, 16 December 2019, https://www.ft.com/content/27c94d40-5c6c-4af1-ad40-c43b5cc691bd.

28. Ibid.

29. 'India's Digital Platforms', *The Economist*, 4 May 2018, https://www.economist.com/special-report/2018/05/04/indias-digital-platforms?gclid=CjwKCAjw2OiaBhBSEiwAh2ZSPy-ajVRZnNmXQX_-Y0neplAgxvfbUuh3bNJI3K6LocJA0s4taXPptRoCjfcQAvD_BwE&gclsrc=aw.ds.

30. Data from *Eight Years with Modi*, Network 18 Media and Investments, p. 50.

31. For 2022 data, see https://pib.gov.in/FeaturesDeatils.aspx?NoteId=151163&ModuleId%20=%202; Our Bureau, 'UPI Transactions Hit Record 657 Crore in Aug', *The Economic Times*, 2 September 2022, https://economictimes.indiatimes.com/news/economy/indicators/upi-transaction-value-touches-rs-10-73-lakh-cr-in-august/articleshow/93921462.cms; https://twitter.com/narendramodi/status/1514141801187364866?s= 20&t=c9ycYb43lAfL6QsEdsrhAg.

32. https://twitter.com/narendramodi/status/1514141801187364866?s= 20&t=c9ycYb43lAfL6QsEdsrhAg.

33. Data from PhonePe's repository of all transactions on the app. Data is representative as PhonePe accounted for approximately 50 per cent of UPI transactions processed. Of course, actual value of transactions in Bengaluru (Rs 8,37,938.7 million) and Noida (Rs 74,371.3 million) is more compared to Sangli (Rs 22,867.6 million) and Rae Bareli (Rs 5,135.5 million).

34. PM Modi's full speech at Digital India Week, 4 July 2022, is available at https://www.youtube.com/watch?v=9E2euLB3hM0.

35. Jasmin B. Gupra, CEO, LXME (India's first neobank for women), quoted in Our Bureau, 'UPI Transactions Hit Record 657 Crore in Aug', *The Economic Times*, https://economictimes.indiatimes.com/news/economy/indicators/upi-transaction-value-touches-rs-10-73-lakh-cr-in-august/articleshow/93921462.cms, 2 September 2022.

36. Real-time payments across businesses and merchants refer to instantaneous digital payments that facilitate the transfer of funds within a few seconds, as opposed to older payment systems such as credit notes or cash that required days to be credited across accounts.

37. Shouvik Das, '40 Percent of Global Real-time Payments Originated in India in 2021: Report', *Mint*, https://www.livemint.com/news/india/40-of-global-real-time-payments-originated-in-india-in-2021-report-11650973119569.html.

38. Full text available at https://www.aciworldwide.com/real-time-payments-report?utm_source=businesswire&utm_medium=press-release&utm_campaign=2022-press-release&utm_content=PT2022-india; for a summary, see ibid. Data also reproduced in *Eight Years with Modi*, Network 18 Media and Investments, p. 50.

39. Times News Network, 'UPI Transactions Hit All-time High of Rs 10.7 Cr in Aug', *The Times of India*, 2 September 2022, https://timesofindia.indiatimes.com/india/upi-transactions-hit-all-time-high-of-rs-10-7-lakh-crore-in-august/articleshow/93938717.cms.

40. Conversation with a senior government official, speaking on condition of anonymity, 6 April 2022.

41. Interview with Rajeev Chandrasekhar, minister of state for Skill Development and Entrepreneurship and Electronics and Information Technology; Rajya Sabha MP, BJP; Spokesperson, BJP, 29 July 2022, Delhi.

42. John Adams, 'These Payment Companies Are Cutting off Russia', *American Banker*, 7 March 2022, https://www.americanbanker.com/payments/list/these-payment-companies-are-cutting-off-russia; Pranav Mukul, 'Explained: Impact of Visa, Mastercard, American Express Block Ban in Russia?' *The Indian Express*, 8 March 2022, https://indianexpress.com/article/explained/explained-impact-of-visa-mastercard-american-express-ban-russia-ukraine-crisis-7804526/.

43. SWIFT, 'An Update to Our Message for the SWIFT Community', 20 March 2022, https://www.swift.com/news-events/news/message-swift-community; European Commission; 'Ukraine: EC Agrees to Exclude Key Russian Banks from SWIFT', 2 March 2022, https://ec.europa.eu/commission/presscorner/detail/en/ip_22_1484.

44. Conversation with a senior official, speaking on condition of anonymity.

45. Quoted in *Global Times*, https://twitter.com/globaltimesnews/status/1515187420274520069?s=08.

46. Anand J. and Sandhya Sharma, 'Why India Is Taking UPI Global', *The Economic Times*, 23 October 2022, https://economictimes.indiatimes.com/why-india-is-taking-upi-global/primearticleshow/94928887.cms?from=mdr.

47. Anand Adhikari, 'The Giant Killer', *Business Today*, 15 September 2022, https://www.businesstoday.in/interactive/longread/upi-the-made-in-india-payments-system-is-rocking-not-just-india-but-is-making-waves-globally-too-171-15-09-2022.

48. Express Web Desk, 'Bhutan Becomes the First Country to Use BHIM UPI,' *The Indian Express*, 14 July 2021, 'https://indianexpress.com/article/business/bhutan-becomes-the-first-neighbouring-country-to-use-bhim-upi-7403970/.

49. On 2 April 2022, https://twitter.com/PMOIndia/status/1510157067864383491?s=08.

50. NPCI, 'BHIM UPI Goes Live at NEOPAY Terminals in UAE', 21 April 2022, https://www.npci.org.in/PDF/npci/press-releases/2022/NIPL-Press-Release-BHIM-UPI-goes-live-at-NEOPAY-terminals-in-UAE.pdf.

51. NPCI, 'India's NPCI International Signs PayXpert as UK's First Acquirer for UPI and RuPay', 18 August 2022, https://www.npci.org.in/PDF/npci/press-releases/2022/NPCI-Press-Release-India%E2%80%99s-NPCI-International-signs-PayXpert-as-UK%E2%80%99s-first-acquirer-for-UPI-and-RuPay.pdf.

52. French Embassy in India, 16 June 2022, https://twitter.com/FranceinIndia/status/1537359650605043712?s=20&t=vQew0R-JbXerntVv_JGTgg.

53. ENS, 'UPI Goes Global: India, Singapore Start Instant Fund Transfer; PM Modi Hails New Era', *The Indian Express*, 22 February 2023, https://indianexpress.com/article/business/banking-and-finance/narendra-

modi-upi-singapore-paynow-launch-8457613/; also see Shayan Ghosh and Gulveen Aulakh, 'Other Nations Interested in India's Payment Channels, Says Indian Finance Minister', *Mint*, 20 September 2022, https://www.livemint.com/industry/banking/other-nations-interested-in-india-s-payment-channels-says-finance-minister-11663660844191.html.

54. Anand J. and Sandhya Sharma, 'Why India Is Taking UPI Global', *The Economic Times*, 23 October 2022, https://economictimes.indiatimes.com/why-india-is-taking-upi-global/primearticleshow/94928887.cms?from=mdr.

55. Quoted in ibid.

56. See, for instance, Hindol Sengupta, Chief Economic Research Officer, Invest India, 'India's Role in Digital Democracy: UPI in France', *The New Indian Express*, 1 July 2022, https://www.newindianexpress.com/opinions/2022/jul/01/indias-role-in-digital-democracy-upi-in-france-2471522.html.

57. Ministry of External Affairs, 'Transcript of Joint Press Interaction Following India-France Ministerial Meeting (14 September 2022), https://www.mea.gov.in/media-briefings.htm?dtl/35715/Transcript_of_Joint_Press_Interaction_following_IndiaFrance_Ministerial_Meeting_September_14_2022.

58. Ministry of External Affairs Annual Report 2021-22, http://www.mea.gov.in/Uploads/PublicationDocs/34894_MEA_Annual_Report_English.pdf.

59. ANI, 'Singapore's Foreign Minister Calls India's Digital Identity a "Clear Opportunity"', *Mint*, 7 August 2022, https://www.livemint.com/technology/tech-news/singapore-foreign-minister-praises-india-s-digital-identity-11659847951127.html.

60. Quoted in Special Correspondent, 'India, Singapore to Link Their Fast Payment Systems UPI & PayNow', *The Hindu*, 14 September 2021, https://www.thehindu.com/business/Industry/india-singapore-to-link-their-fast-payment-systems-upi-paynow/article36446835.ece.

61. Interview with Rajeev Chandrasekhar, minister of state for Skill Development and Entrepreneurship and Electronics and Information Technology; Rajya Sabha MP, BJP; Spokesperson, BJP, 29 July 2022, Delhi.

62. PIB, NITI Aayog, '90 Days of Digi Dhan Mela: Towards Making Digital Payments a Mass Movement', 30 March 2017, https://pib.gov.in/newsite/PrintRelease.aspx?relid=160219.

63. Interview with Saurabh Kumar, director, Ministry of Finance, New Delhi, 6 April 2022. Kumar was private secretary (2019–21) and additional private secretary (2014–19) to minister for Communication and IT and Law and Justice Communications. He was additional commissioner, GST, at the time of the interview.

64. Ibid.

65. Ibid.

66. Ibid.

67. Conversation with a government official, speaking on condition of anonymity, 6 April 2022.

68. Andy Mukherjee, 'Fintech's Everywhere in India: Banks Need a Counterattack', *Bloomberg*, 31 March 2022, https://www.bloomberg.com/opinion/articles/2022-03-30/payment-apps-have-the-upper-hand-in-india-but-banks-can-counterattack.

69. Author's interview with Caesar Sengupta, Google vice president, Next Billion Users and Digital Payments, at Google HQ in May 2019, published as '95% of Video Consumption in India Is in Regional Languages; Hindi Internet Users Will Outnumber English by 2021', *The Times of India*, 17 May 2019, https://timesofindia.indiatimes.com/blogs/academic-interest/95-of-video-consumption-in-indiais-in-regional-languages-hindi-internet-users-will-outnumber-english-usersby-2021/.

70. Interview with Vivek Wadhwa, New Delhi, 12 September 2022.

71. Vivek Wadhwa, Ismail Amla and Alex Salkever, 'As Silicon Valley Fantasises About Web3, India Leaps Ahead on Payments', *Fortune*, 30 June 2022, https://fortune.com/2022/06/30/blockchain-india-upi-payments-global-reach/.

72. Digbijay Mishra and Tarush Bhalla, 'NPCI Pings Govt, Industry on UPI Market Share', *The Economic Times*, 20 September 2022, https://economictimes.indiatimes.com/tech/technology/npci-pings-govt-industry-on-upi-market-share-cap/articleshow/94310588.cms?from=mdr.

73. Vivek Wadhwa, Ismail Amla and Alex Salkever, 'As Silicon Valley Fantasises About Web3, India Leaps Ahead on Payments', *Fortune*,

30 June 2022, https://fortune.com/2022/06/30/blockchain-india-upi-payments-global-reach/.

74. All arguments here summarised from ibid.

75. For more on this debate which started after an RBI consultation paper see, Team TOI Plus, 'Why the Government Should Not Impose a Fee on UPI', *The Times of India*, 26 August 2022, https://timesofindia.indiatimes.com/business/india-business/why-the-government-should-not-impose-a-fee-on-upi/articleshow/93781089.cms.

76. https://twitter.com/FinMinIndia/status/1561367751658192897?s=20&t=ZPhM3J9u5Cv1CVLGIp9wdg.

77. MEA, 'India's Forthcoming G20 Presidency', 13 September 2022, https://www.mea.gov.in/press-releases.htm?dtl/35700/Indias_forthcoming_G20_Presidency.

78. Quoted in Anil Padmanabhan, 'Beyond Bollywood & Yoga: DPGs, India's New Soft Power, About to Be on Show', *The Economic Times*, 6 October 2022, https://economictimes.indiatimes.com/opinion/et-commentary/beyond-bollywood-yoga-dpgs-indias-new-soft-power-about-to-be-on-show/articleshow/94667272.cms?from=mdr.

79. Mark Isakowitz, vice president, Government Affairs and Public Policy, US & Canada, Google's Submission on 'Federal Reserve Actions to Support Interbank Settlement of Faster Payments, Docket No. OP – 1670', to Ann Misback, secretary, Board of Governors of the Federal Reserve System, Federal Reserve Financial Services Policy Committee, 7 November 2019.

80. Interview with Saurabh Kumar, director, Ministry of Finance, New Delhi, 6 April 2022. Kumar was private secretary (2019–21) and additional private secretary (2014–19) to minister for Communication and IT and Law and Justice Communications. He was additional commissioner, GST, at the time of the interview.

81. Mugdha Variyar's interview with T. Koshy, CEO, ONDC, 'I Believe New E-commerce Policy Will Consider How ONDC Will Evolve and Mature: CEO T Koshy', *The Economic Times*, 9 October 2022, https://economictimes.indiatimes.com/prime/technology-and-startups/i-believe-the-e-commerce-policy-will-consider-how-ondc-will-evolve-and-mature-ceo-t-koshy/primearticleshow/94605728.cms.

82. See, for instance, this thread, https://twitter.com/Ravisutanjani/status/1575822319750352896?s=20&t=QEmVnXP95eKHTJWL

yvb_BQ. Also see Our Bureau, 'UPI, AA, ONDC to Rejig Supply Chain', *The Economic Times*, 21 September 2022.

83. See, for instance, this thread, https://twitter.com/nikhilkumarks/status/1529355001197654017?s=20&t=XKTrDPHYk7UNquxRb7zXNQ.

84. PIB, Ministry of Commerce, 'Shri Piyush Goyal Chaired Open Network for Digital Commerce', 17 August 2021, https://pib.gov.in/PressReleasePage.aspx?PRID=1745611.

85. Suraksha P., 'The Network Effect', *The Economic Times*, 21 August 2022, p. 8.

86. Saurabh Sinha, 'Centre Likely to Unveil E-comm Platform This Month', *The Times of India*, 7 September 2022, https://timesofindia.indiatimes.com/business/india-business/centre-likely-to-unveil-e-comm-platform-this-month/articleshow/94062775.cms.

87. Gopika Gopakumar, 'UPI Payments to Now Have Credit Card Option', *The Hindustan Times*, 21 September 2022, p. 16.

88. Anand Adhikari, 'The Giant Killer', *Business Today*, 15 September 2022, https://www.businesstoday.in/interactive/longread/upi-the-made-in-india-payments-system-is-rocking-not-just-india-but-is-making-waves-globally-too-171-15-09-2022.

89. Ibid.

90. A. Michael Spence's interview with Srijana Mitra Das, 'The Global Economy Is Undergoing a "Regime Change" Today—India Is the Outstanding Performer Now', *The Economic Times*, 29 September 2022, https://economictimes.indiatimes.com/news/et-evoke/the-global-economy-is-undergoing-a-regime-change-today-india-is-the-outstanding-performer-now/articleshow/94542579.cms?utm_source=contentofinterest&utm_medium=text&utm_campaign=cppst. Also see the comments by RBI Governor Shaktikanta Das. 'UPI has emerged as the pride of the nation … It's one area where I think India can play a major leadership role in the world in the days to come. It's a phenomenal product, but we need to be extremely watchful of its infrastructure as it scales', quoted in Manish Singh, 'UPI Supercharged Mobile Payments in India. It's Now Gearing up for Next Phase of Growth', *Techcrunch*, 21 September 2022, https://techcrunch.com/2022/09/21/upi-supercharged-mobile-payments-in-india-its-now-gearing-up-for-next-phase-of-growth/.

91. https://www.linkedin.com/posts/abhishpatil_fact-candy-brands-owned-the-chutta-activity-6984065792543727616-K8ub?utm_source=share&utm_medium=member_desktop.

92. See, for instance, Vivek Punj, 'How True Is Viral Claim of UPI Killing Toffee', *BQPrime*, 14 October 2022, https://www.bqprime.com/business/how-true-is-viral-claim-of-upi-killing-toffee-business; Pushpita Dey, 'No, UPI Is Not Alone in Fall of Candy Sales in India', *Zee Business*, 31 October 2022, https://www.zeebiz.com/india/news-upi-alone-is-not-behind-the-fall-in-candy-sales-in-india-205446; Sanya Jain, 'Is UPI Killing the Toffee Business? The Numbers Say Otherwise for Lotte India', Moneycontrol.com, 14 October 2022, https://www.moneycontrol.com/news/trends/is-upi-killing-the-toffee-business-the-numbers-say-otherwise-for-lotte-india-9330161.html.

6. NUTS AND BOLTS

1. Data from minister of state for Communications Devusinh Chauhan, response to Rajya Sabha Unstarred Question No. 1983, 23 December 2022, available at chrome-extension://efaidnbmnnnibpcajpcglclefindmkaj/https://pqars.nic.in/annex/258/AU1983.pdf.

2. Data from Ministry of Communications, PIB, *Year-end Review 2022: Ministry of Communications*, 16 December 2022, https://pib.gov.in/PressReleasePage.aspx?PRID=1884072; Ministry of Communications, PIB, *Year-end Review 2022: Ministry of Communications*, 27 December 2021, https://www.pib.gov.in/PressReleseDetailm.aspx?PRID=1785452; TRAI, *Indian Telecom Services Performance Indicators, January–March 2014*, available at https://www.trai.gov.in/release-publication/reports/performance-indicators-reports?field_start_date_value%5Bvalue%5D&page=4; TRAI, *Telecom Sector in India: Decadal Profile*, https://www.trai.gov.in/sites/default/files/NCAER–Report08june12.pdf.

3. This belief in hard-wired tech connectivity was articulated at a function at PM Narendra Modi's official residence, 7 Lok Kalyan Marg, where he presided over the launch of an edited collection of papers put together by scholars at the Carnegie Endowment of World Peace positing an economic reforms blueprint for India. INVC Desk, 'Cities in the Past were Built on Riverbanks: Narendra Modi', 8 June

2014, https://www.internationalnewsandviews.com/cities-in-the-past-were-built-on-river-banks-narendra-modi/.

4. See, for instance, Deloitte, FICCI, DOT, *Broadband Infrastructure for Transforming India*, 2016, available at https://www2.deloitte.com/content/dam/Deloitte/in/Documents/technology-media-telecommunications/in-tmt-broadband-infrastructure-for-transforming-india-noexp.pdf.

5. See, for instance, Tom Gerencer, 'Top 10 Advantages of Fiber Optic Internet Connections', HP Tech Takes, 21 April 2020, https://www.hp.com/us-en/shop/tech-takes/top-10-advantages-fiber-optic-internet-connections; '5 Reasons Why Professionals Choose Fiber Optic Cables Instead of Copper', 21 March 2022, https://www.cxtec.com/blog/5-reasons-professionals-choose-fiber-optic-cables-instead-copper/; Tom Collins. '5 Reasons Why Fiber May be the Best for Your Business', *Atlantech Online*, 27 July 2022, https://www.atlantech.net/blog/fiber-optic-internet-vs-cable. Also see Telecommunication Engineering Centre, Department of Telecommunications, Ministry of Communications, Government of India, *Concept Paper on Optical Fibre and Cable in Indian Telecom Network*, November 2021, available at https://www.tec.gov.in/pdf/Studypaper/Concept%20paper%20on%20OFC.pdf.

6. Quoted in Robin Jeffrey and Assa Doron, *The Great Indian Phone Book: How Cheap Mobile Phones Change Business, Politics and Daily Life* (London: Hurst, 2013), pp. 137–8.

7. Robin Jeffrey and Assa Doron, *The Great Indian Phone Book: How Cheap Mobile Phones Change Business, Politics and Daily Life* (London: Hurst, 2013), p. 246, in Notes. The reference they cite is to Andrew Blum, *Tubes: A Journey to the Center of the Internet* (New York: Ecco, 2012), pp. 1–2, 264.

8. Data from Parliamentary question response by Rajeev Chandrasekhar, minister of state for Electronics and Information Technology, in 'Common Services Centres Under CSC 2.0 Project', Unstarred Question No. 4680, Answered in Lok Sabha, 29 March 2023. Also data from https://csc.gov.in/.

9. Full text of Narendra Modi's Independence Day speech on 15 August 2020 is available at https://news.abplive.com/news/india/independence-day-2020-full-text-of-pm-modis-speech-to-nation-from-the-ramparts-of-red-fort-1313291.

10. *Report of Committee on National Fibre Optical Network (NOFN)*, 31 March 2015, p. 10, available at https://dot.gov.in/sites/default/files/Report%20of%20the%20Committee%20on%20NOFN.pdf p. 10 https://pib.gov.in/PressReleaseIframePage.aspx?PRID=1646111.

11. Interview with Saurabh Kumar, director, Ministry of Finance, New Delhi, 6 April 2022. Kumar was private secretary (2019–21) and additional private secretary (2014–19) to minister for Communication and IT and Law and Justice Communications. He was additional commissioner, GST, at the time of the interview.

12. Nalin Mehta, *India on Television: How Satellite News Channels Changed the Ways We Think and Act* (New Delhi: HarperCollins, 2008), pp. 299–300.

13. Interview with Saurabh Kumar, director, Ministry of Finance, New Delhi, 6 April 2022. Kumar was private secretary (2019–21) and additional private secretary (2014–19) to minister for Communication and IT and Law and Justice Communications. He was additional commissioner, GST, at the time of the interview.

14. As on 30 June 2023, https://transformingindia.mygov.in/performance-dashboard/#primary.

15. Anirban Sarma, 'The BBNL-BSNL Merger: A Faltering Force Meets an Immovable Object', India Matters, ORF, 13 June 2022, https://www.orfonline.org/expert-speak/the-bbnl-bsnl-merger-a-faltering-force-meets-an-immovable-object/; S. Ronendra Singh, 'Bharat Calling: BSNL-BBNL Merger Close to Finishing Line', *Business Standard*, 24 November 2022, https://www.thehindubusinessline.com/info-tech/bsnl-bbnl-merger-close-to-finalisation/article66174627.ece.

The OFC also led to a brief political slugfest. In early 2021, the opposition Congress demanded a probe into BharatNet for what it termed 'poor maintenance work' and for sub-contracting decisions taken by it after a critical preliminary draft report by the Comptroller and Auditor General (CAG) of India. The BJP's former Union minister Ravi Shankar Prasad responded by terming the allegations as false and misleading. He said the CAG audit report was a preliminary one, to which the Ministry had given a 'suitable response' ahead of the final report and that all decisions were taken with the consent of the Digital Communications Commission. See Special Correspondent, 'Congress Demands Probe After CAG Flags Irregularities', *The Hindu*,

17 July 2021, https://www.thehindu.com/news/national/congress-demands-probe-after-cag-flags-irregularitiesa-in-bharatnet-project/article35382644.ece; Special Correspondent, 'Congress Allegations are Misleading, Says Ravi Shankar Prasad', *The Hindu*, 18 July 2021, https://www.thehindu.com/news/national/congress-allegations-misleading-ravi-shankar-prasad/article35394946.ece.

16. Ministry of Communications, PIB, 'Progress of National Broadband Mission', 22 July 2022, https://pib.gov.in/PressReleasePage.aspx?PRID=1843752.

17. Kaush Arha, 'India at the Centre of the Indian Ocean Submarine Cable Network: Trusted Connectivity in Practice', Issue Brief No. 630, ORF, April 2023, https://www.orfonline.org/research/india-at-the-centre-of-the-indian-ocean-submarine-cable-network/#_edn5.

18. Ibid.

19. RIL Media Release, 17 May 2021, available at chrome-extension://efaidnbmnnnibpcajpcglclefindmkaj/https://www.ril.com/getattachment/366d722e-4d86-4d5b-922a-3322da07dc66/India-at-the-Center-of-Two-New-Subsea-Cable-System.aspx; Swarajya Staff, 'Reliance to Build 16000 Kilometers Long Submarine Cable System to Connect India with South East Asia Middle East and Europe', *Swarajya*, 18 May 2021, https://swarajyamag.com/insta/reliance-to-build-over-16000-kms-long-submarine-cable-system-to-connect-india-with-south-east-asia-middle-east-and-europe.

20. Mohd Saroon, 'Jio's Undersea Cable Projects Get Nod from Environment Ministry's Expert Committee', 19 November 2022, https://cablecommunity.com/jios-undersea-cable-projects-get-nod-from-environment-ministrys-expert-committee/.

21. Niharika Sharma, 'Why Mukesh Ambani Is Building an International Undersea Cable System?' *QZ*, 2 June 2021, https://qz.com/india/2014815/why-is-ambanis-reliance-building-a-submarine-cable-network.

22. Airtel Media Release, 21 February 2022, https://www.airtel.in/press-release/02-2022/airtel-joins-sea-me-we-6-undersea-cable-consortium-to-scale-up-high-speed-network-for-indias-emerging-digital-economy.

23. Sidhartha, 'Smartphone Surge: Exports of Electronics Pips Garments', *The Times of India*, 17 April 2023, https://timesofindia.indiatimes.com/business/india-business/smartphone-surge-exports-of-electronics-pip-garments/articleshow/99544156.cms?from=mdr.

24. Ibid.

25. Surajeet Das Gupta, 'Localisation Plan: Indian Firms to Make Key Components for Apple', *Business Standard*, 19 April 2023, https://www.business-standard.com/companies/news/apple-likely-to-get-two-key-components-made-by-indian-companies-123041801006_1.html.

26. Data quoted in Kiran Rathee, 'Bumper Apple Harvest: Phone FY23 Exports Jump 4X to Top $5b', *The Economic Times*, 12 April 2023, https://economictimes.indiatimes.com/news/economy/foreign-trade/bumper-apple-harvest-iphone-fy23-exports-jump-4x-to-top-5-billion/articleshow/99419853.cms.

27. Express News Service, 'Ashwini Vaishnaw: If You Want to Go Green, Then We as a Country Must Invest Significantly in Railways', *The Indian Express*, 28 June 2023, https://indianexpress.com/article/india/ashwini-vaishnaw-if-you-have-to-go-green-then-we-as-a-country-must-invest-significantly-in-railways-8689571/.

28. Subhrojit Mallick, 'Apple Likely to Make More iPhones in India This Year', *The Economic Times*, 6 September 2022, https://economictimes.indiatimes.com/news/india/apple-likely-to-make-more-iphones-in-india-this-year/articleshow/94012636.cms.

29. Rahul Chauhan, Rohit Lamba and Raghuram Rajan, 'Has India Really Become a Mobile Phone Manufacturing Giant?' *The Wire*, republished from Raguram Rajan's LinkedIn page on 1 June 2023, https://thewire.in/trade/india-mobile-phone-manufacturing-giant-assembly.

30. Surajeet Das Gupta, 'Localisation Plan: Indian Firms to Make Key Components for Apple', *Business Standard*, 19 April 2023, https://www.business-standard.com/companies/news/apple-likely-to-get-two-key-components-made-by-indian-companies-123041801006_1.html.

31. See, for instance, ICREAR, ICEA, *Globalise to Localise: Exporting at Scale and Deepening the Ecosystem Are Vital to Higher Domestic Value Additions in Electronics*, 2022, pp. 5–6, available at https://icrier.org/pdf/Globalise_to_Localise.pdf.

7.   INDIA'S TECHADE: WHAT'S NEXT ON DIGITAL FUTURES?

1. Samir Saran and Sharad Sharma, 'Digital Public Infrastructure: Lessons from India', 7 February 2023, UNESCO Inclusive Policy Lab, https://en.unesco.org/inclusivepolicylab/analytics/digital-public-

infrastructure-%E2%80%93-lessons-india. For Account Aggregator Framework, see Ministry of Finance, PIB, 'Know All About Account Aggregator Network: A Financial Data Sharing System', 10 September 2021, https://pib.gov.in/PressReleaseIframePage. aspx?PRID=1753713. For more on DEPA, see Siddharth Tiwary, Frank Packer and Rahul Matthan, 'Data for People, By People', Finance and Development, IMF, March 2023, https://www.imf.org/ en/Publications/fandd/issues/2023/03/data-by-people-for-people-tiwari-packer-matthan; Vikas Kathuria, 'Data Empowerment and Protection Architecture: Concept and Assessment', ORF Brief, Issue 487, August 2021, https://www.orfonline.org/research/data-empowerment-and-protection-architecture-concept-and-assessment/.

2.   Siddharth Tiwary, Frank Packer and Rahul Matthan, 'Data for People, By People', Finance and Development, IMF, March 2023, https://www.imf.org/en/Publications/fandd/issues/2023/03/data-by-people-for-people-tiwari-packer-matthan.

3.   Samir Saran and Sharad Sharma, 'Digital Public Infrastructure: Lessons from India', 7 February 2023, UNESCO Inclusive Policy Lab, https://en.unesco.org/inclusivepolicylab/analytics/digital-public-infrastructure-%E2%80%93-lessons-india.

4.   Siddharth Tiwary, Frank Packer and Rahul Matthan, 'Data for People, By People', Finance and Development, IMF, March 2023, https://www.imf.org/en/Publications/fandd/issues/2023/03/data-by-people-for-people-tiwari-packer-matthan.

5.   Samir Saran and Sharad Sharma, 'Digital Public Infrastructure: Lessons from India', 7 February 2023, https://samirsaran.com/2023/02/07/digital-public-infrastructure-lessons-from-india/; For (Open Credit Enablement Network, see https://indiastack.org/open-networks.html; for Open Network for Digital Commerce, see https://ondc.org/; for Open Health Services Network (UHI), see https://uhi.abdm.gov.in/.

6.   Siddharth Tiwary, Frank Packer and Rahul Matthan, 'Data for People, By People', Finance and Development, IMF, March 2023, https://www.imf.org/en/Publications/fandd/issues/2023/03/data-by-people-for-people-tiwari-packer-matthan.

7.   Surajeet Das Gupta, 'Telecom Milestone: At 50 Million, India has 5% of World's 5G Subscribers', Business Standard, 27 March 2023, https://www.business-standard.com/industry/news/a-milestone-at-50-million-india-has-5-of-world-s-5g-customers-123032600219_1.html.

8. Speaking at The ET Global Summit, 18 February 2023. Video available at https://twitter.com/ETNOWlive/status/1626844239111020549?s=20.

9. Pankaj Doval, 'Only Indian Tech Will Power BSNL's 4G, 5G Upgrade: Govt', *The Times of India*, 15 August 2022. Also see https://www.businesstoday.in/latest/economy/story/make-in-india-how-government-owned-c-dot-designed-the-core-network-architecture-of-5g-348899-2022-10-03.

10. Ministry of Communications, PIB Release, 1 October 2022, https://pib.gov.in/PressReleasePage.aspx?PRID=1864252.

11. PIB, 'BSNL Enhances 4G Features', 3 July 2023, https://pib.gov.in/PressReleasePage.aspx?PRID=1937698; Romita Majumdar, ET Tech, 'TCS To Pocket Bulk of Rs 15,000 Crore BSNL Order', *The Economic Times*, 23 May 2023, https://economictimes.indiatimes.com/tech/information-tech/tcs-to-bag-bulk-of-rs-15000-crore-bsnl-order/articleshow/100433196.cms.

12. Kiran Rathee, ET Bureau, '5G Stack Fully Developed, Ready to be Exported: DOT', *The Economic Times*, 1 March 2023, https://economictimes.indiatimes.com/industry/telecom/telecom-news/india-5g-stack-fully-developed-ready-to-be-exported-dot/articleshow/98330625.cms.

13. Quoted in Romita Majumdar and Kalpana Pathak, 'RIL Builds Indigenous 5G Tech, Says Ready to Take on World', *Mint*, 16 July 2020, https://www.livemint.com/companies/news/ril-builds-indigenous-5g-tech-says-ready-to-take-on-world-11594863752689.html. Also see Tech Desk, 'Reliance Jio "Made in India" 5G Solution Announced at RIL AGM 2020: Details Inside', *The Indian Express*, 16 July 2020, https://indianexpress.com/article/technology/tech-news-technology/reliance-jio-to-launch-made-in-india-5g-network-mukesh-ambani-6506961/; Reliance Jio Release, 24 June 2021, https://www.jio.com/platforms/resource-center/press-release/made-in-india-5g-solution.

14. Ayushi Kar, 'End of the American Internet: India-China Contribute to 50% World's Data Traffic', *Hindu BusinessLine*, 4 December 2022, https://www.thehindubusinessline.com/info-tech/end-of-american-internet-india-china-contribute-to-50-of-worlds-data-traffic/article66222842.ece.

15. RBI Bulletin December 2022, p. 140.

16. Ibid., p. 143.

17. PTI, 'KV Kamath Says Digital Economy Can Contribute 25% GDP by FY29', *The Economic Times*, 26 February 2023, https://economictimes. indiatimes.com/industry/banking/finance/kv-kamath-says-digital-economy-can-contribute-25-gdp-by-fy29/articleshow/98248649. cms?from=mdr.

18. Ministry of Electronics and Information Technology, India's Trillion Dollar Digital Opportunity, available at https://meity.gov.in/ writereaddata/files/india_trillion-dollar_digital_opportunity.pdf.

19. The Hindu Bureau, 'Internet Economy to Become 12-13% of GDP by 2030: Report', *The Hindu*, 6 June 2023, https://www.thehindu.com/ business/Economy/indias-digital-economy-to-grow-over-fivefold-to-1-trillion-by-2030-international-report/article66937186.ece.

20. NDTV, 'What Amazon, Google and Microsoft Announced After PM's "Hi-Tech" Handshake', 24 June 2023, https://www.ndtv.com/india-news/major-announcements-from-us-tech-giants-after-pm-modis-hi-tech-handshake-4148612; TBS Report, 'What 3 US Tech Giants Announced After Modi's Hi-Tech Handshake', 24 June 2023, https:// www.tbsnews.net/world/south-asia/what-3-us-tech-giants-announced-after-modis-hi-tech-handshake-655514.

21. See, for instance, the series of articles on this in *The Economic Times* between September and December 2022: Manoj Joshi, 'Chipping Away at Beijing', 28 October 2022; Subimal Bhattacharjee, 'The Chips are Getting High: US Gets Its Act Together in Denying China Technology', 21 October 2022, https://economictimes.indiatimes. com/opinion/et-commentary/the-chips-are-getting-high-us-gets-its-act-together-in-denying-china-technology/articleshow/94995876. cms?from=mdr; Shashi Shekhar Vempati, 'Get Chip Off the Shoulder: The Case for Turning Atmanirbhar in Silicon-making', 26 September 2022, https://economictimes.indiatimes.com/ opinion/et-commentary/get-chip-off-the-shoulder-the-case-for-turning-aatmanirbhar-in-silicon-making/articleshow/94439767. cms?from=mdr; Pranab Dal Samanta, 'Geopolichips Going Nuclear', 1 November 2022 , https://economictimes.indiatimes.com/opinion/et-commentary/why-india-needs-to-be-a-player-in-global-semiconductor-order/articleshow/95213727.cms?from=mdr; Saibal Dasgupta, 'Semiconducting This War', 22 December 2022; Swaminathan S. and Anklesaria Aiyar, 'Hold On To Your Chips, India', 21 September 2022.

22   MEITY, Presentation made during the Digital India Dialogues on the proposed Digital India Act on 9 March in Bengaluru, Karnataka. Available at https://www.meity.gov.in/content/digital-india-act-2023.

23.   Available at https://mib.gov.in/sites/default/files/IT%28Intermediary%20Guidelines%20and%20Digital%20Media%20Ethics%20Code%29%20Rules%2C%202021%20English.pdf.

24.   Available at https://www.meity.gov.in/writereaddata/files/Information%20Technology%20%28Certifying%20Authority%29.pdf.

25.   See https://www.cert-in.org.in/.

26.   Availableathttps://meity.gov.in/writereaddata/files/GSR313E_10511%281%29_0.pdf.

27   Availableathttps://www.meity.gov.in/writereaddata/files/Information%20Technology%20%28%20Procedure%20and%20safeguards%20for%20blocking%20for%20access%20of%20information%20by%20public%29%20Rules%2C%202009.pdf.

28.   Available at https://www.meity.gov.in/writereaddata/files/The%20Digital%20Personal%20Data%20Potection%20Bill%2C%202022_0.pdf; for a critical analysis and timeline, see also Rishi Dev, 'An Analysis of the Digital Personal Data Protection Bill', *Live Law*, 23 June 2023, https://www.livelaw.in/articles/an-analysis-of-the-digital-personal-data-protection-bill-231161.

29.   See Rajeev Chandrasekhar's tweet on this: https://twitter.com/Rajeev_GoI/status/1668221201075023873?s=20; Bindu Shajan Perappadan, 'COWIN Vaccination Data Out, Centre Denies Breach', *The Hindu*, 12 June 2023, https://www.thehindu.com/news/national/health-ministry-responds-to-massive-cowin-data-breach/article66960250.ece.

30.   For a critical analysis on this, see Gautam Chikarmane, 'Aadhaar Breach is Serious But Bigger Challenge is Data and Privacy Protection Law', ORF, 5 June 2018, https://www.orfonline.org/expert-speak/aadhaar-breach-serious-bigger-challenge-data-privacy-protection-law/.

31.   See, for example, R.S. Sharma, 'Truth Fears No Trolls', *The Indian Express*, 9 August 2019, https://indianexpress.com/article/opinion/columns/rs-sharma-aadhaar-number-challenge-twitter-trai-chairman-data-protection-5298308/; R.S. Sharma 'Why I Gave Out My Aadhaar Number', *The Indian Express*, 1 August 2018, https://indianexpress.com/article/opinion/columns/rs-sharma-aadhaar-number-challenge-trai-chairman-twitter-5283781/; Varad Pandey and R.S. Sharma, 'Aadhar 10 Years On', *The Indian Express*, 19 December 2019,

https://indianexpress.com/article/opinion/columns/aadhaar-10-years-on-6173890/.

32. See https://meity.gov.in/writereaddata/files/National-Data-Governance-Framework-Policy.pdf; also see Frontline News Desk, 'Explained: Can the National Data Governance Policy be a Game Changer', *Frontline*, 1 February 2023, https://frontline.thehindu.com/news/explained-can-the-national-data-governance-policy-be-a-gamechanger/article66459872.ece.

33. For a timeline and some of the issues raised, see Sarvesh Mathi, 'National Data Governance Policy: What is It and What Are Some of the Concerns Around It', *MediaNama*, 2 February 2023, https://www.medianama.com/2023/02/223-national-data-governance-policy-what-is-it-concerns-around-it/.

34. K. Puttaswamy v Union of India: Writ Petition (Civil) No 494 of 2012, Supreme Court of India judgment (24 August 2017), http://supremecourtofindia.nic.in/supremecourt/2012/35071/35071_2012_Judgement_24-Aug-2017.pdf.

35. See, for instance, Soumyendra Barik, 'Data Protection Bill Approved by Cabinet: Content, Concerns', *The Indian Express*, 6 July 2023, https://indianexpress.com/article/explained/explained-economics/data-protection-bill-approved-by-cabinet-content-concerns-8780035/; Andy Mukherjee, 'India's Data Protection Bill Has a Privacy Problem', *Bloomberg*, 22 November 2020, https://www.bloomberg.com/opinion/articles/2022-11-22/india-s-digital-personal-data-protection-bill-puts-privacy-at-risk#xj4y7vzkg.

36. Apar Gupta, 'Digital Data Protection Bill Uses Brevity and Vagueness to Empower Government, Undermine Privacy', *The Indian Express*, 25 November 2022, https://indianexpress.com/article/opinion/columns/apar-gupta-writes-digital-data-protection-bill-brevity-vagueness-empower-government-undermine-privacy-8279134/.

37. Speaking at a Digital India Dialogue in Mumbai. Quoted in Vallari Sanzgiri, 'Digital India Consultation: Why Does Rajeev Chandrasekhar Want to Remove Safe Harbour?' *MediaNama*, 24 May 2023, https://www.medianama.com/2023/05/223-digital-india-act-rajeev-chandrasekhar-safe-harbour/.

38. In a television debate on the Digital India Act on News9, 27 June 2023, available at https://www.youtube.com/watch?v=lEV4h_vZMxw.

39. These suggestions are from Samir Saran and Sharad Sharma, 'Digital Public Infrastructure: Lessons from India', 7 February 2023, UNESCO Inclusive Policy Lab, https://en.unesco.org/inclusivepolicylab/analytics/digital-public-infrastructure-%E2%80%93-lessons-india.

40. See, for instance, Umang Poddar, 'Digital India Bill May Change the Internet as We Know It', *Scroll*, 24 March 2023, https://scroll.in/article/1045731/the-proposed-digital-india-bill-may-change-the-internet-as-we-know-it; Aarthi Ganesan, 'How Can the Digital India Act Develop a Transparent and Fair Content Regulation Framework?', *MediaNama*, 25 May 2023, https://www.medianama.com/2023/05/223-digital-india-act-transparent-fair-content-regulation-framework-nama/.

41. Quoted in Arun Mohan Sukumar, *Midnight's Machines: A Political History of Technology in India* (New Delhi: Penguin Random House, 2019), p. 30.

ACKNOWLEDGEMENTS

This book has only been possible because of the help and support of several people. Prof. Robin Jeffrey in Melbourne and Prof. Assa Doron in Canberra read multiple drafts, and their encouragement and sage advice was invaluable at every point. In Singapore, Rishabh Srivastava provided the data tools and the incisive dashboards that informed much of the analysis in this book. In Delhi, Prof. Sanjeev Singh and Sanjiv Shankaran picked up the phone at odd hours, were a solid sounding board and offered helpful suggestions on the draft. In Bengaluru, T.M. Veeraraghav provided much-needed help with interviews and pointed out errors in early drafts. Pradeep Nagarkoti and Rajiv Pundir did a lot of the field work.

Santosh Menon at Network18 was generous with his support and advice. Many of the ideas in this book were catalysed in stimulating conversations with him on Digital India. Brajesh Kumar Singh saved several snafus that he immediate spotted in the proofs and also provided perspective.

Vikas Singh and Sharvani Pandit remain constant pillars of support, in ways too myriad to list here.

At my academic home at UPES, Sharad Mehra, Ram Sharma and Sunil Rai smoothened many paths to provide an enabling environment and the mental space to finish this project.

A sincere, heartfelt thank you to everyone who agreed to be interviewed for this book, to others who gave me deep background or facilitated access to many previously closed doors. Some of you are named in the preceding pages. Apologies for not naming others here for paucity of space and other obvious reasons, but you know who you are.

Jaya Bhattacharji Rose, my literary agent, remained a rock and compass in more ways than one.

V.K. Karthika, my editor, pulled out all the stops to meet an impossible deadline, in a way that only she can, making the book better than it was with her razor-sharp editing. Sonia Madan meticulously copyedited the text. A big thank you to Jojy Philip, Saurabh Garge and the whole Westland team.

Nitika Mansingh, who remains the sky and the earth, bravely put up with yet another project and allowed it to happen. This book simply wouldn't have been possible without her. Rakesh Mehta and Madhu Bala have been stoic and supportive as ever, asking every day if it was finished. A big thanks also to Arjun, Raghav, Miranda and Nitin Mehta.

I am truly fortunate to have had a great deal of support. Any errors, of course, are mine alone.